KAISER CHIEFS 'Employment'

WISE PUBLICATIONS
part of The Music Sales Group

London / New York / Paris / Sydney / Copenhagen / Berlin / Madrid / Tokyo

Published by
Wise Publications,
8/9 Frith Street, London, W1D 3JB, England.

Exclusive distributors:
Music Sales Limited,
Distribution Centre, Newmarket Road, Bury St Edmunds,
Suffolk, IP33 3YB, England.

Music Sales Pty Limited,
120 Rothschild Avenue, Rosebery,
NSW 2018, Australia.

Order No. AM982938
ISBN 1-84609-080-6
This book © Copyright 2005 by Wise Publications,
a division of Music Sales Limited.

Music arrangements by Scott Brown.
Music processed by Paul Ewers Music Design.

Printed in the United Kingdom.

www.musicsales.com

Your Guarantee of Quality:
As publishers, we strive to produce every book
to the highest commercial standards.

The music has been freshly engraved. Particular care has been
given to specifying acid-free, neutral-sized paper made from pulps
which have not been elemental chlorine bleached.

This pulp is from farmed sustainable forests
and was produced with special regard for the environment.

Throughout, the printing and binding have been planned to ensure a sturdy,
attractive publication which should give years of enjoyment.

If your copy fails to meet our high standards, please inform us
and we will gladly replace it.

Everyday I Love You Less and Less

Words & Music by Nicholas Hodgson, Richard Wilson,
Andrew White, James Rix & Nicholas Baines

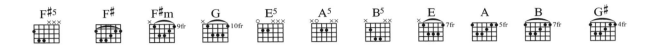

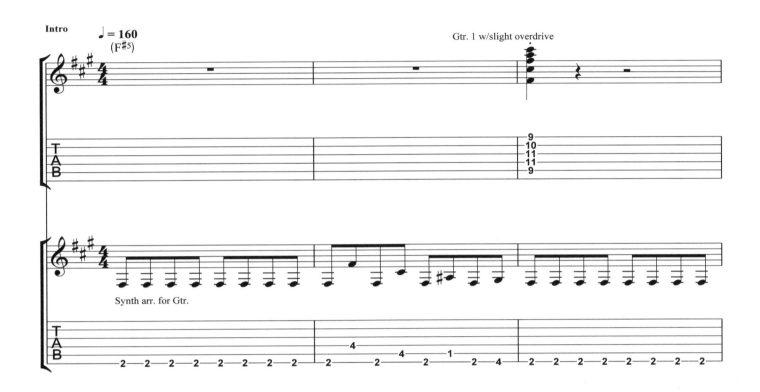

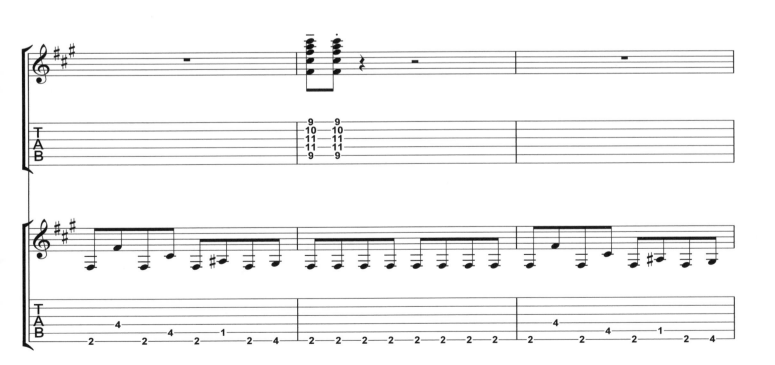

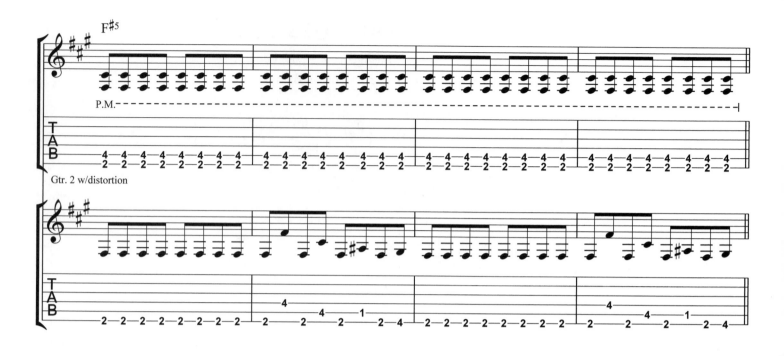

Gtr. 2 w/distortion

Verse

Ev -'ry day I love you less and less. It's clear to see that you've be - come ob -

-sessed. I've got to get this mes -sage to the press, that

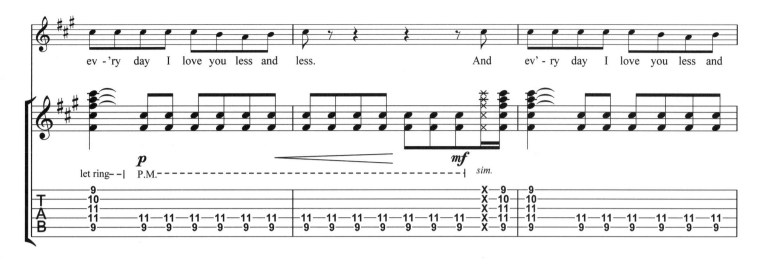

ev-'ry day I love you less and less. And ev'-ry day I love you less and

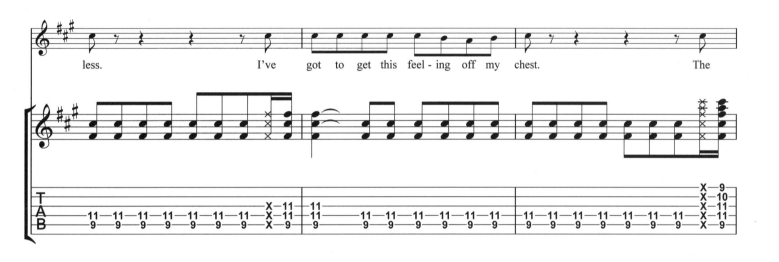

less. I've got to get this feel-ing off my chest. The

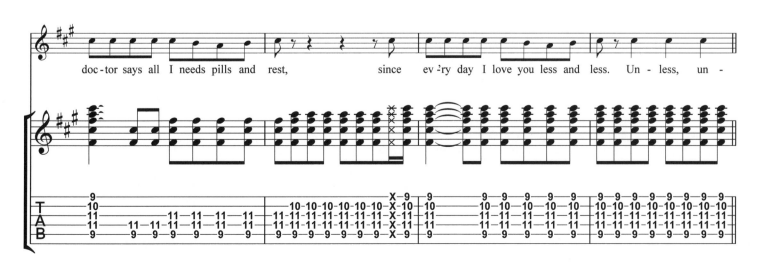

doc-tor says all I needs pills and rest, since ev'-ry day I love you less and less. Un - less, un -

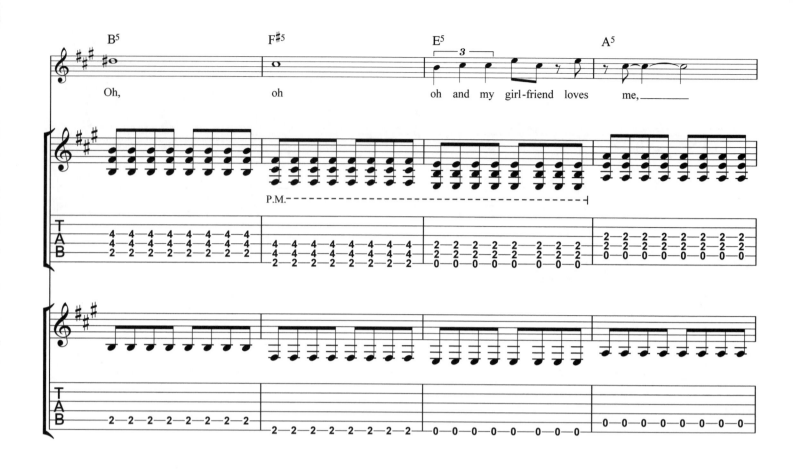

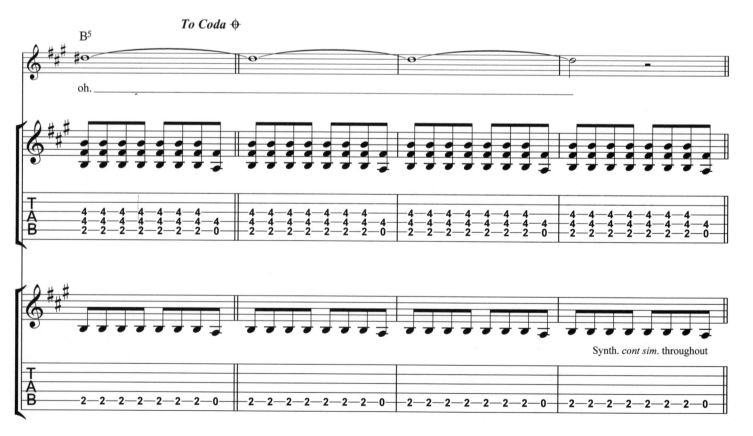

Verse 2

Ev -'ry day I love you less and less. I can't be-lieve once you and me did

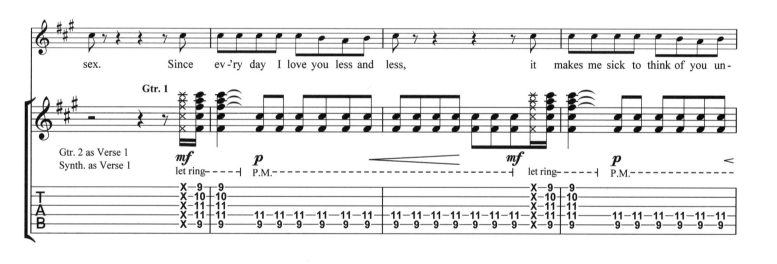

sex. Since ev -'ry day I love you less and less, it makes me sick to think of you un-

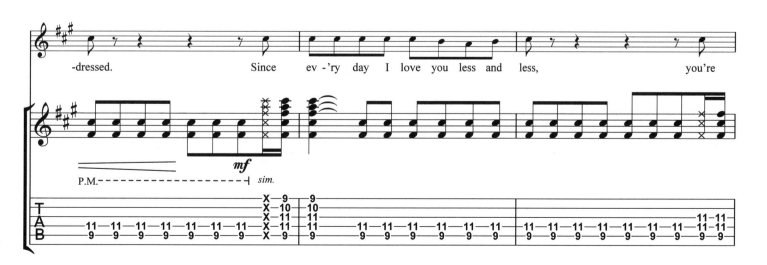

-dressed. Since ev -'ry day I love you less and less, you're

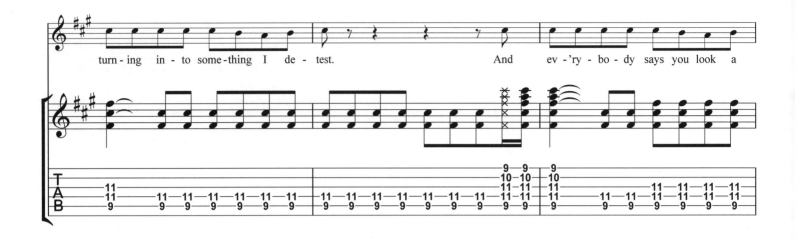

D.S. al Coda

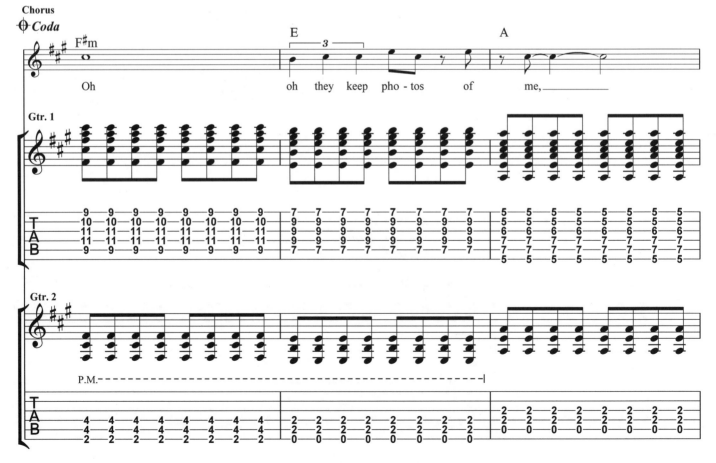

10

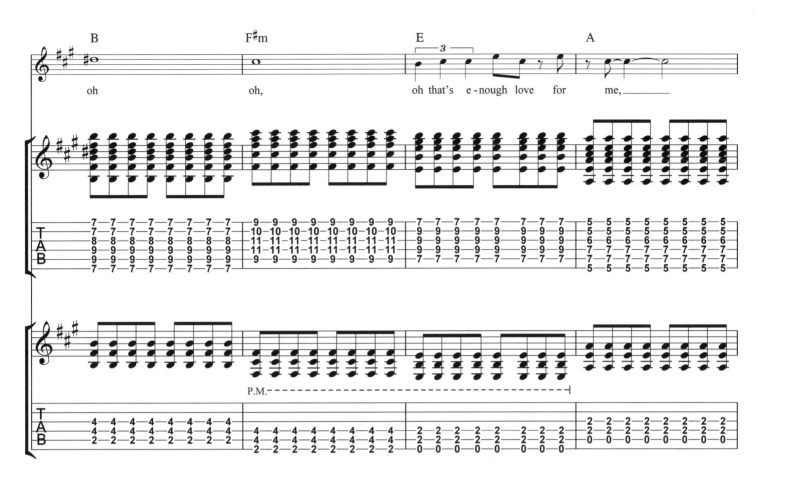

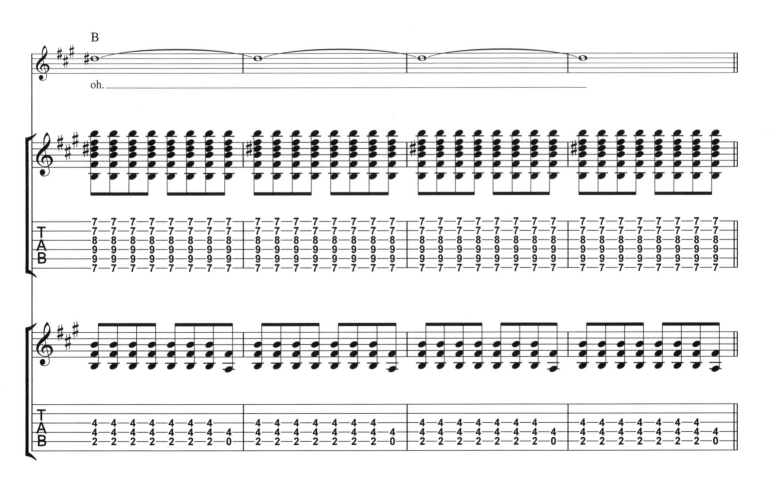

Breakdown
Half-time feel

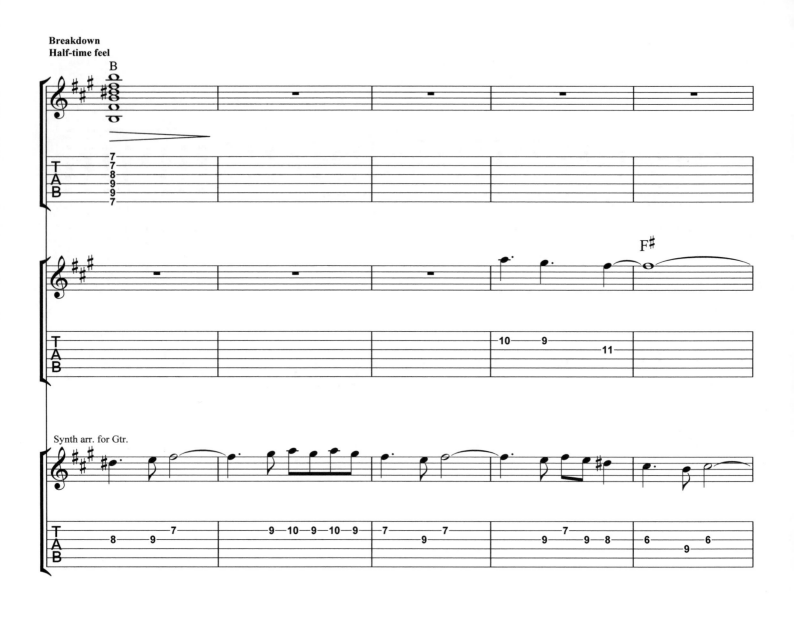

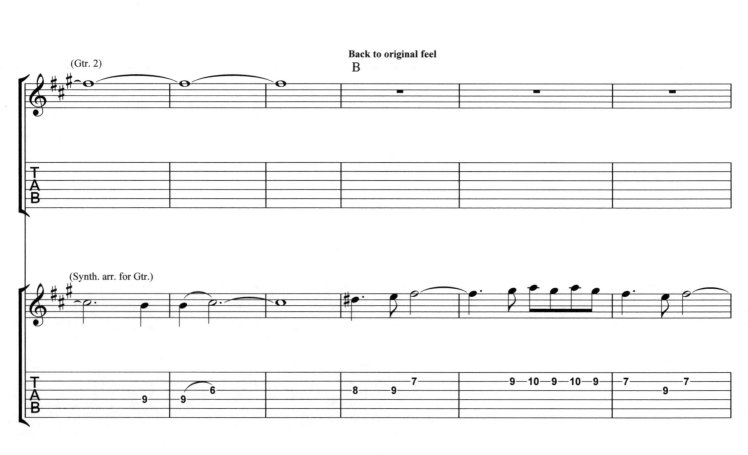

12

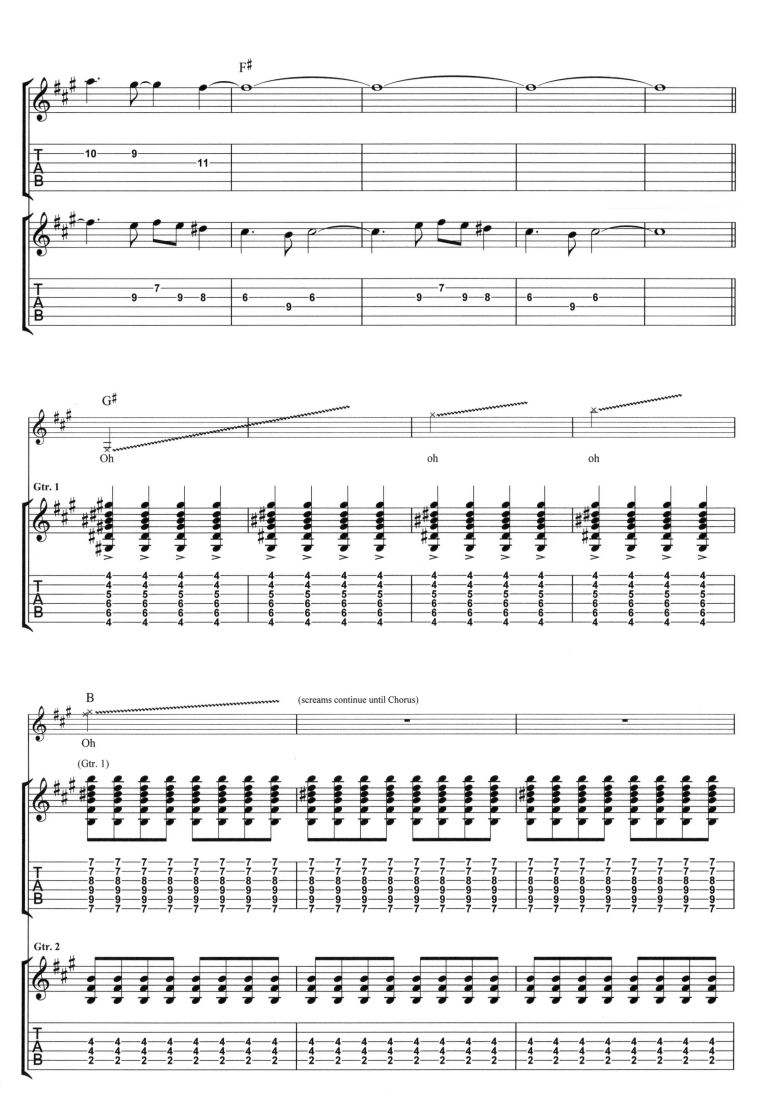

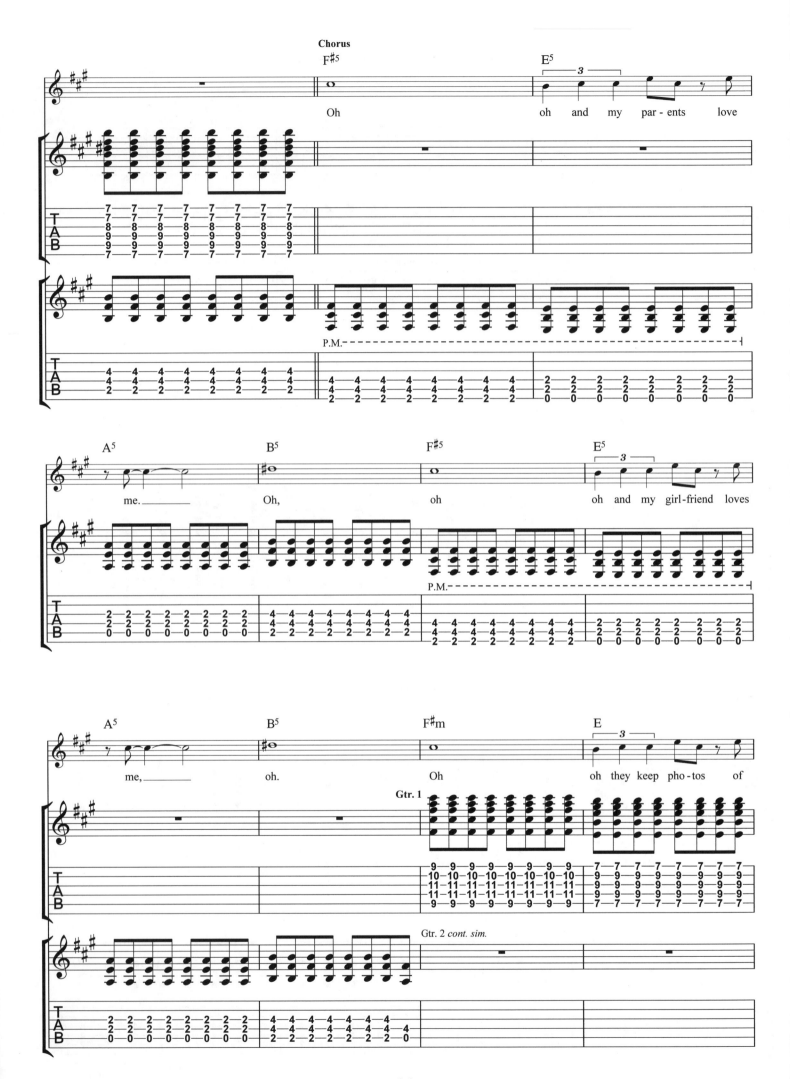

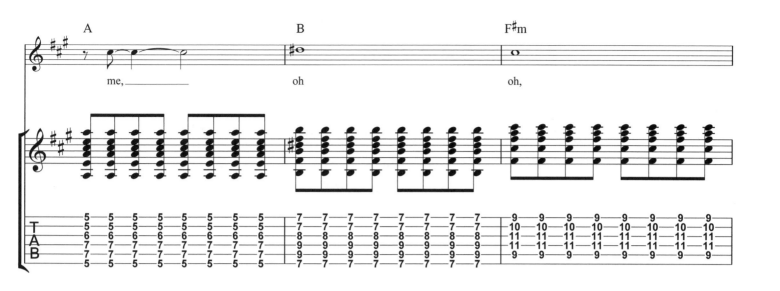

me, _____ oh oh,

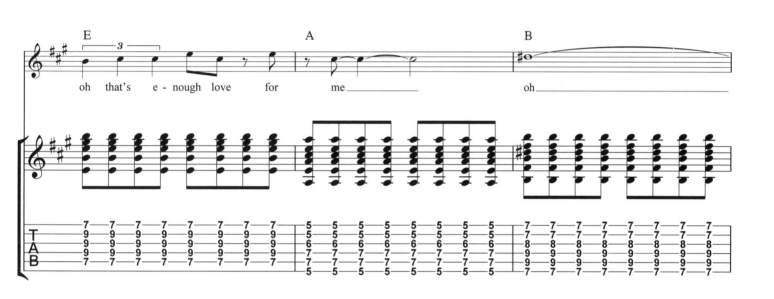

oh that's e - nough love for me _____ oh _____

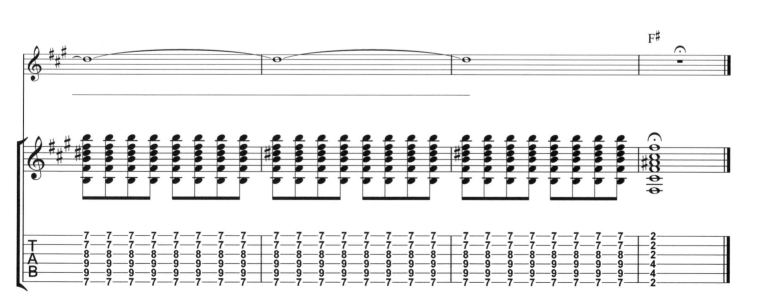

I Predict A Riot

Words & Music by Nicholas Hodgson, Richard Wilson,
Andrew White, James Rix & Nicholas Baines

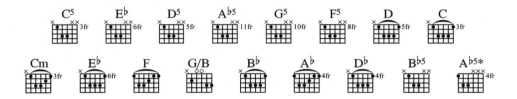

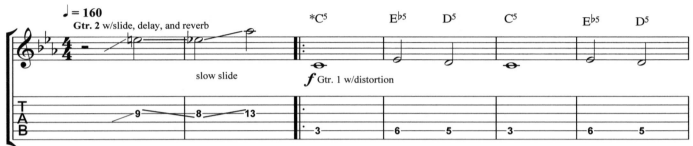

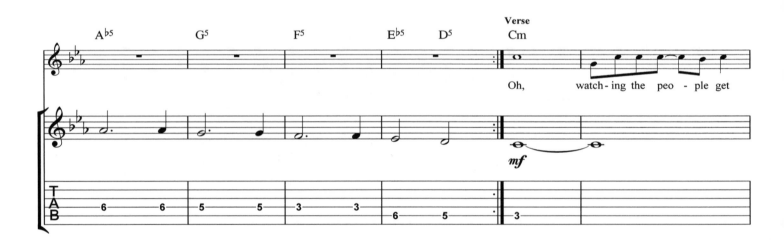

*Chords implied by harmony throughout except where indicated.

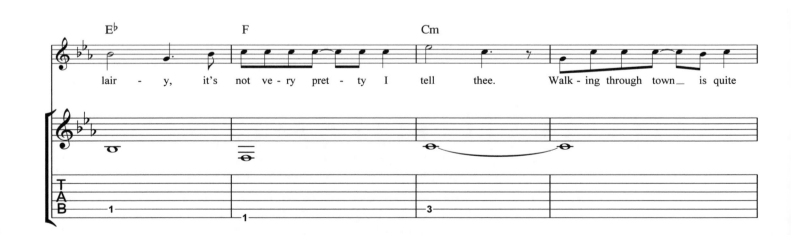

Verse

Oh, I tried to get to my ta - xi, the man in the track - suit at - tacks me. He said that he saw it be - fore me and wants things to get things a bit go - ry. Girls scrab - ble round with no clothes on to bor - row a pound for a con - dom. If it was - n't for chip fat they'd be froz - en, they're not ve - ry sen - si - ble. Ah ah ah

Pre-chorus

18

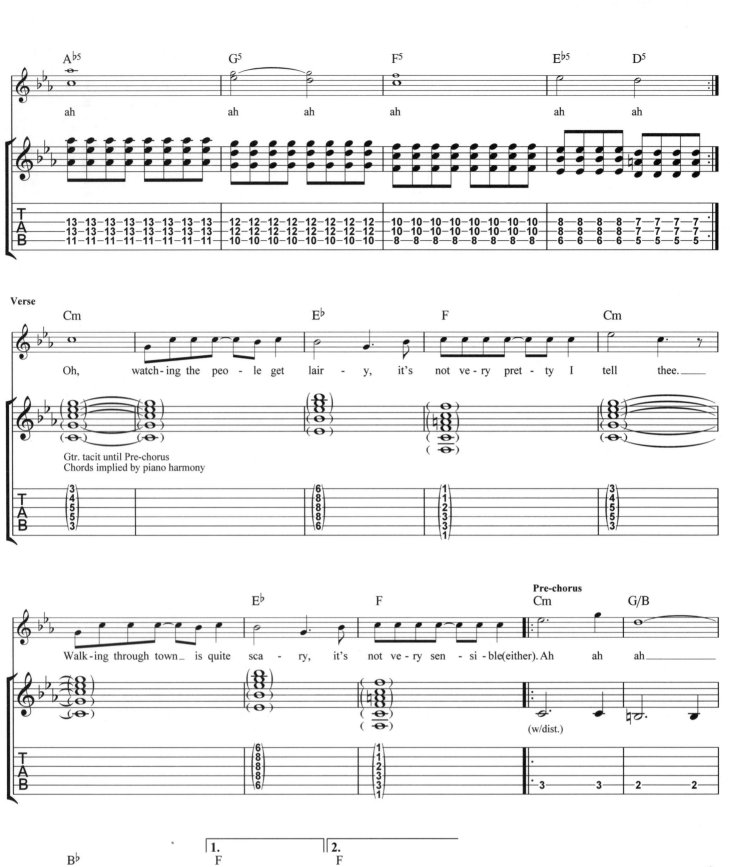

Verse

Oh, watch-ing the peo-le get lair - y, it's not ve-ry pret-ty I tell thee.____

Gtr. tacit until Pre-chorus
Chords implied by piano harmony

Walk-ing through town___ is quite sca-ry, it's not ve-ry sen - si -ble(either). Ah   ah   ah_____

Pre-chorus

(w/dist.)

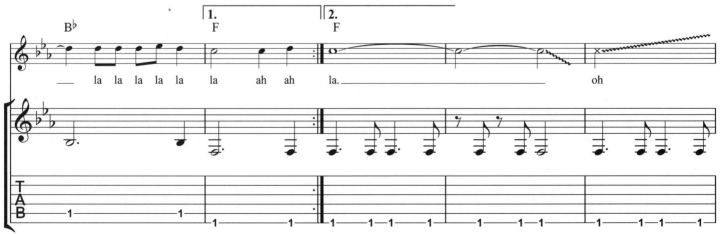

____ la   la   la la   la   la   ah ah   la._____   oh

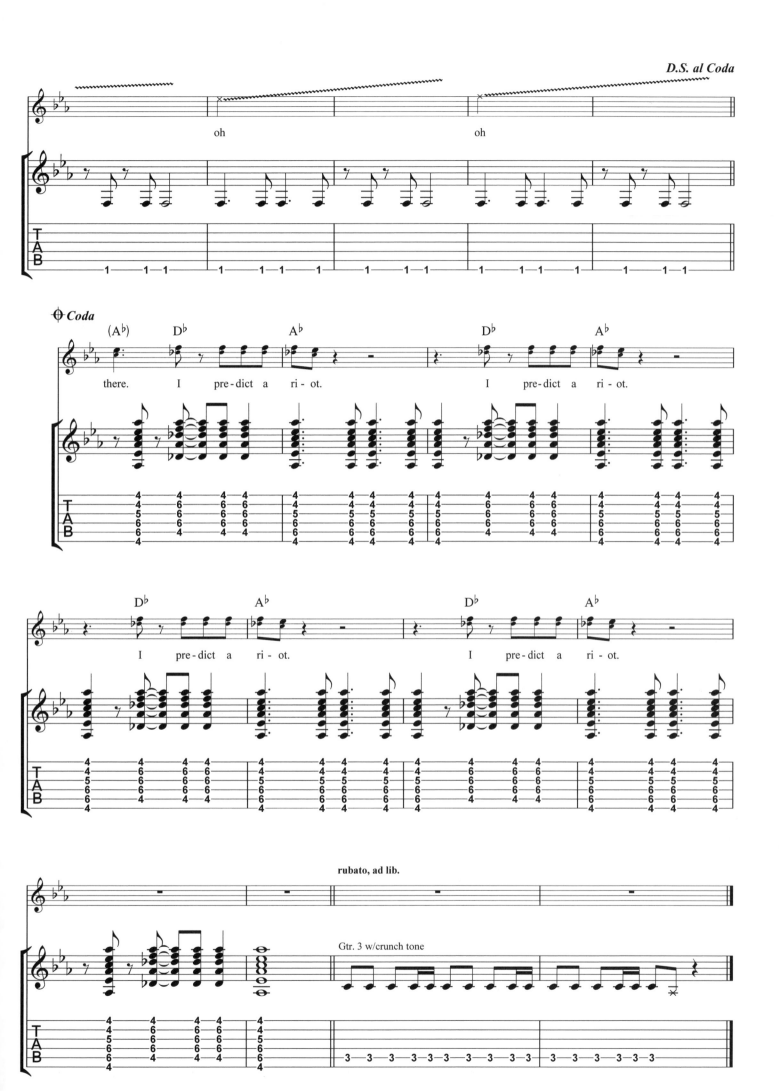

Modern Way

Words & Music by Nicholas Hodgson, Richard Wilson, Andrew White, James Rix & Nicholas Baines

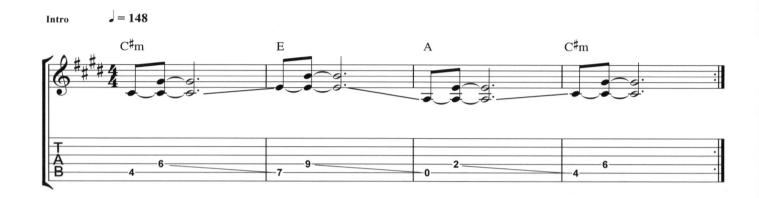

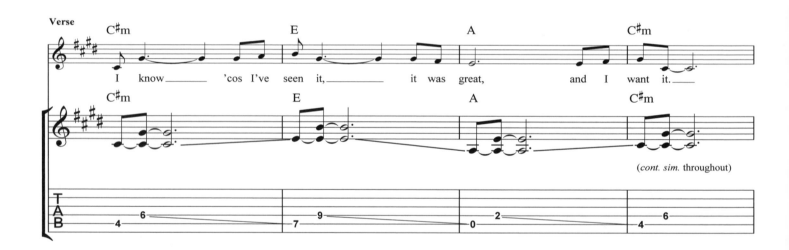

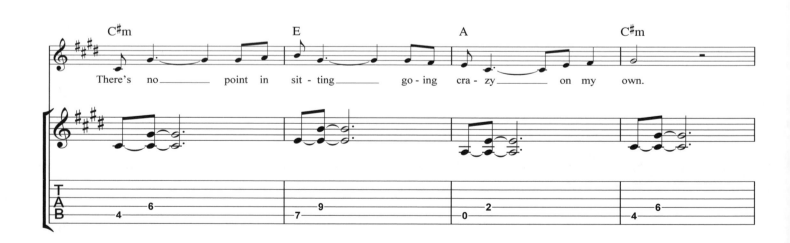

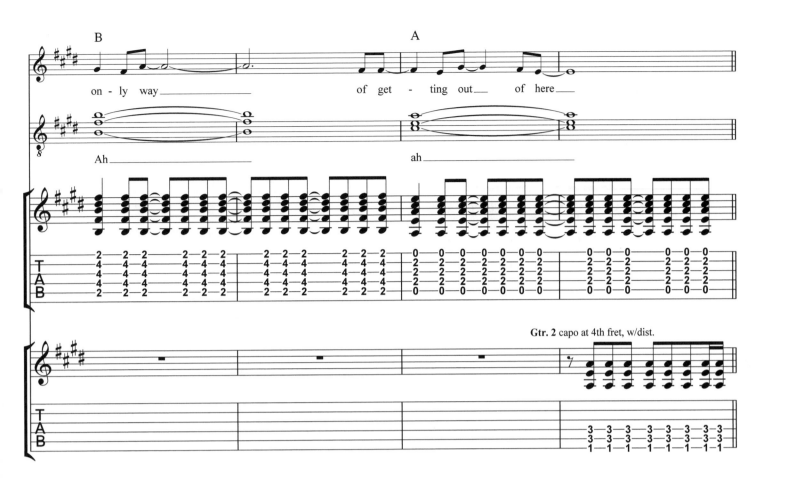

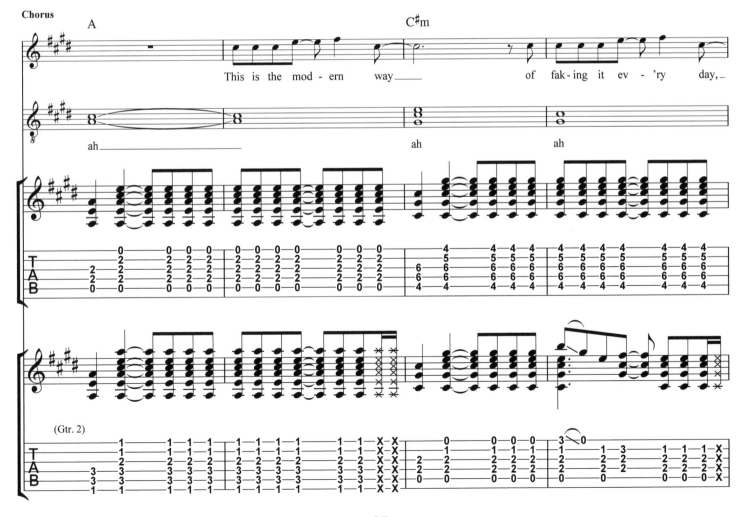

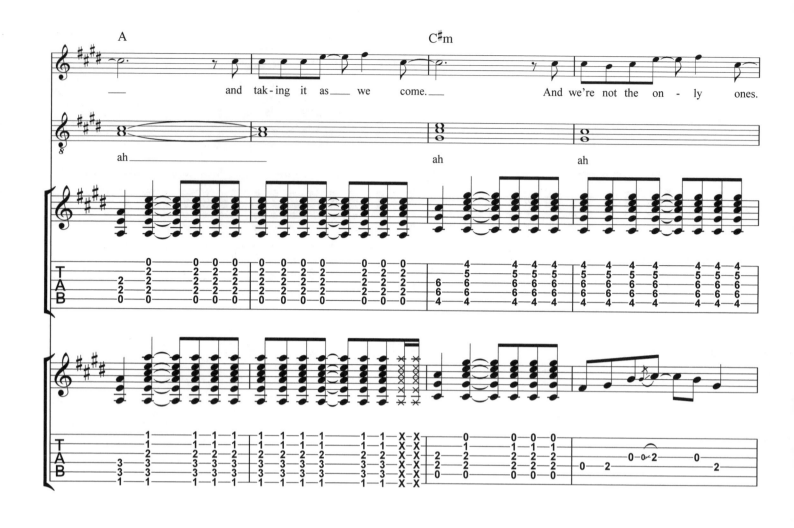

and tak-ing it as__ we come.__ And we're not the on - ly ones.

ah_____ ah ah

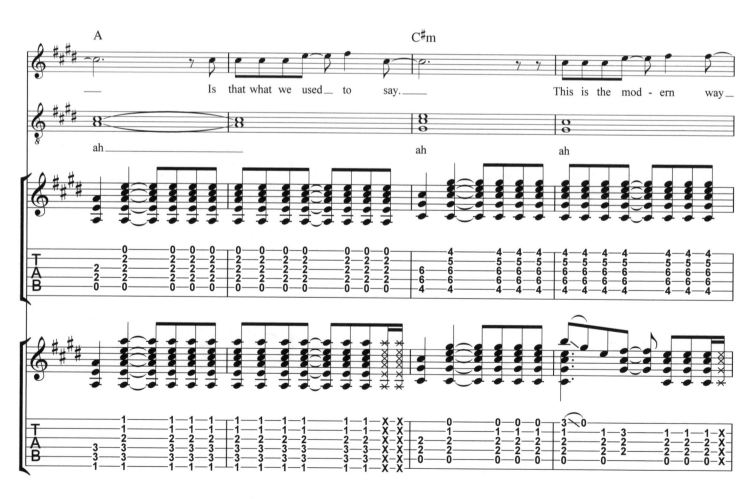

Is that what we used__ to say.__ This is the mod - ern way__

ah_____ ah ah

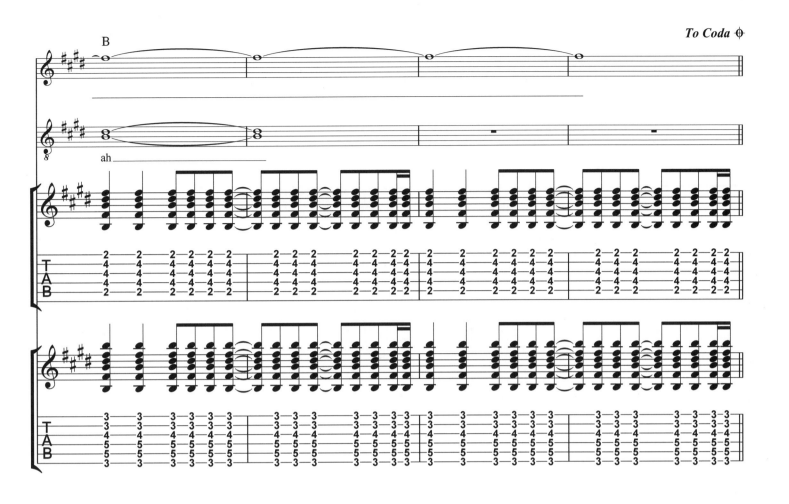

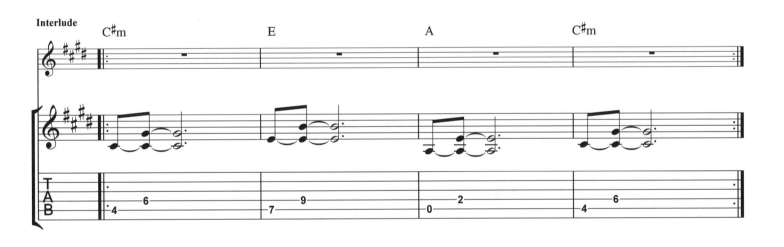

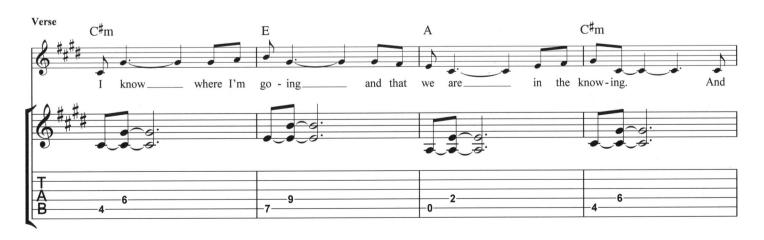

27

I will_____ stop at no-thing_____ just to get_____ what I want. It's the

Chorus

Coda

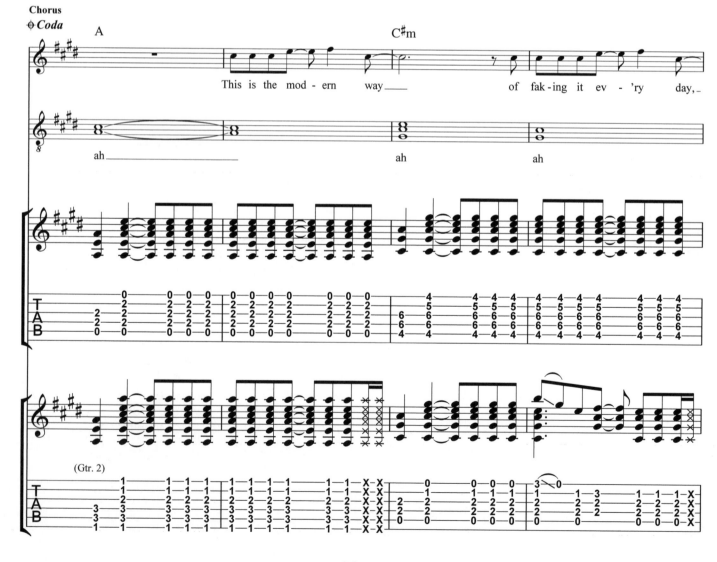

This is the mod-ern way_____ of fak-ing it ev-'ry day,_

ah_____ ah ah

(Gtr. 2)

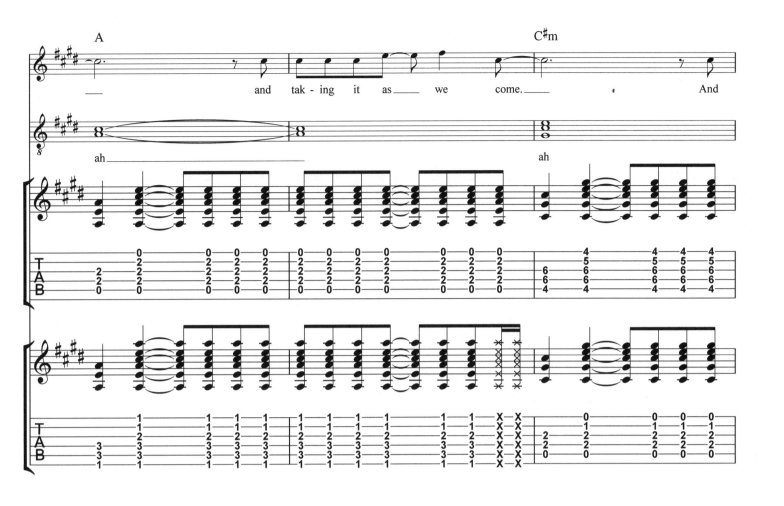

and tak - ing it as ___ we come. ___   And

ah ___   ah

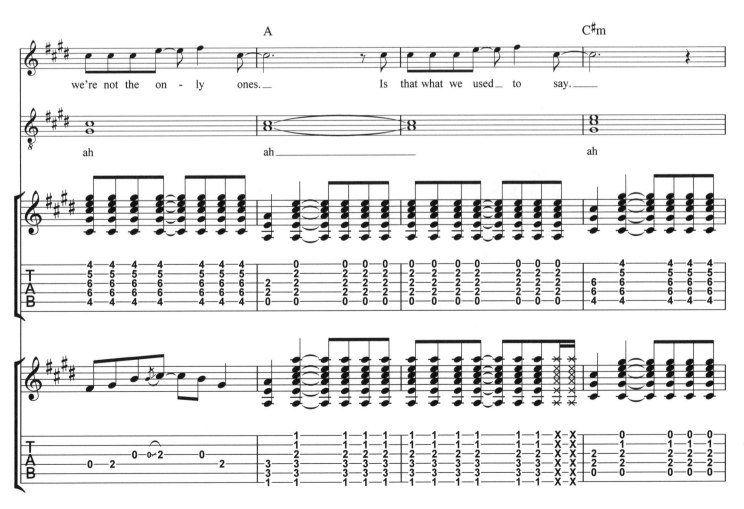

we're not the on - ly ones. ___   Is that what we used ___ to say. ___

ah   ah ___   ah

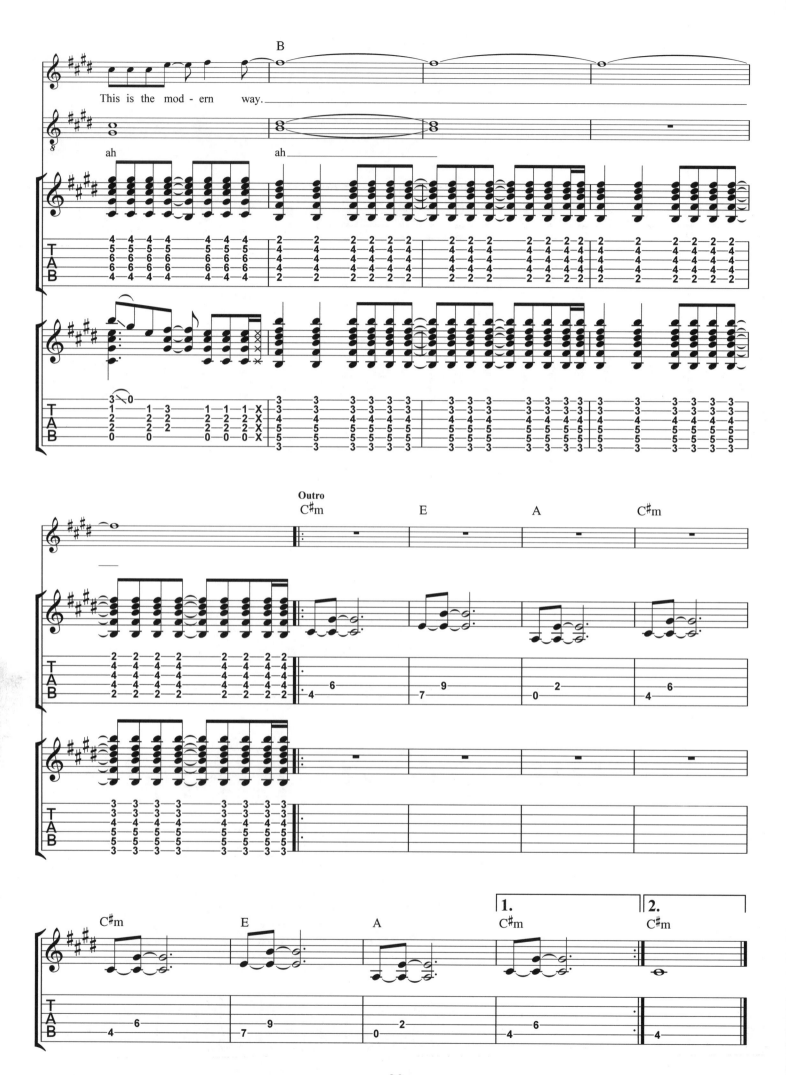

Na Na Na Na Naa

Words & Music by Nicholas Hodgson, Richard Wilson,
Andrew White, James Rix & Nicholas Baines

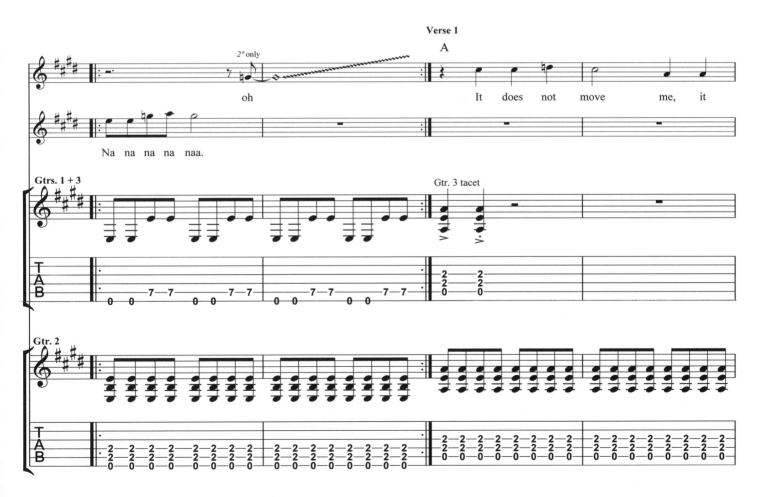

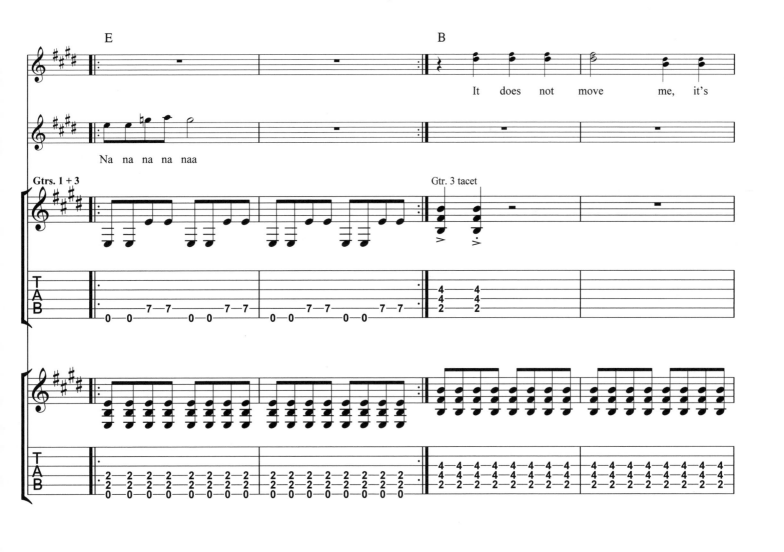

It does not move me, it's

Na na na na naa

not the kind of thing that I like.

Na na na na naa.

33

Verse 2

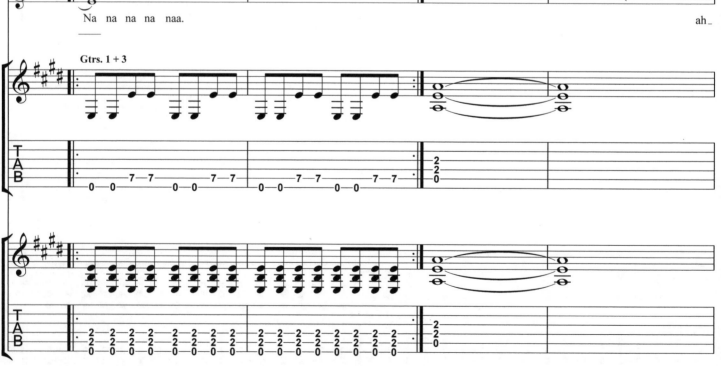

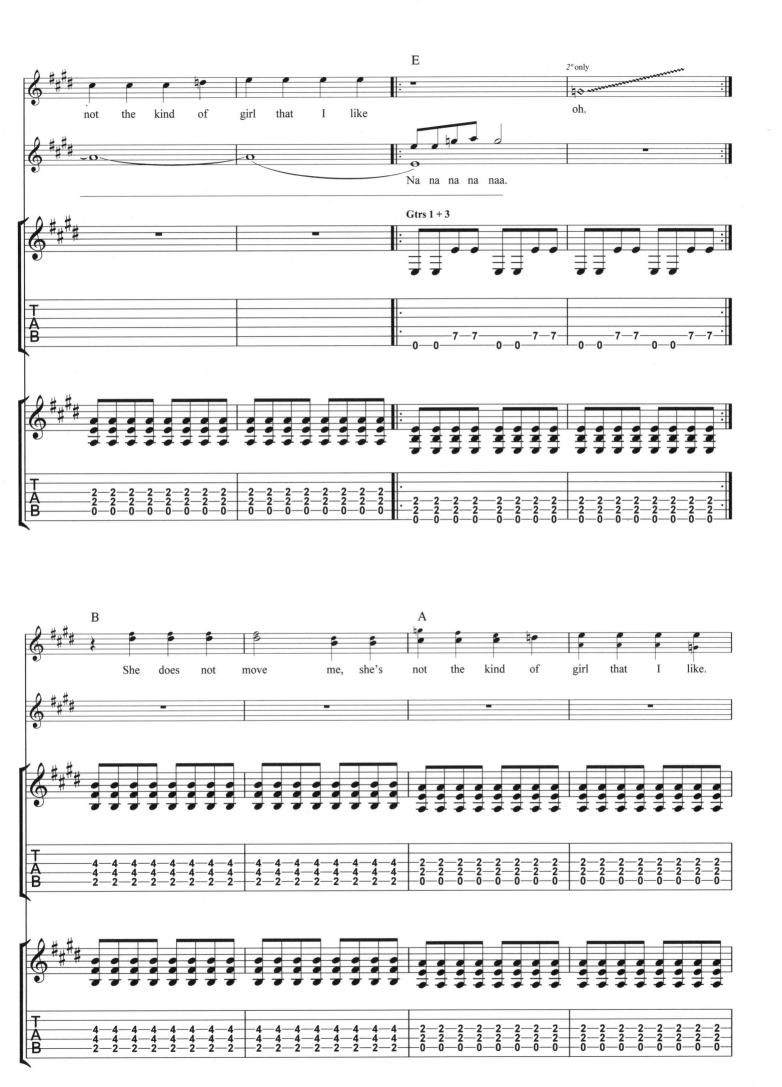

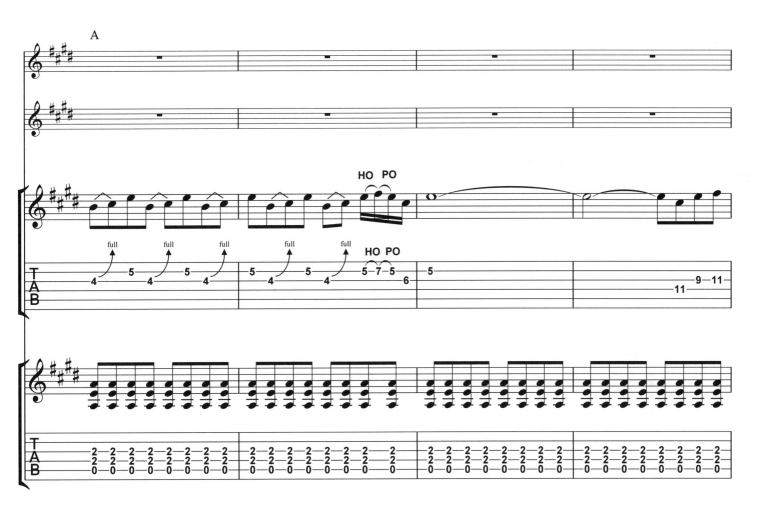

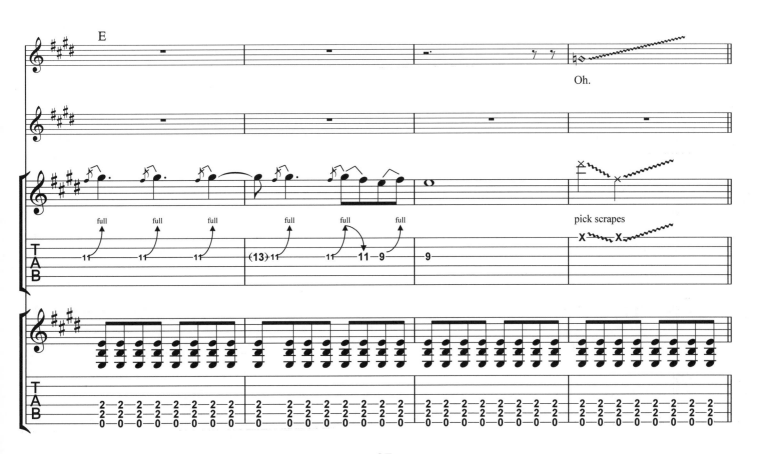

It does not move me, it's not the kind of thing that I like.

Na na na na naa.

Na na na na naa.

oh____

2° only

Gtrs. 1 + 3

38

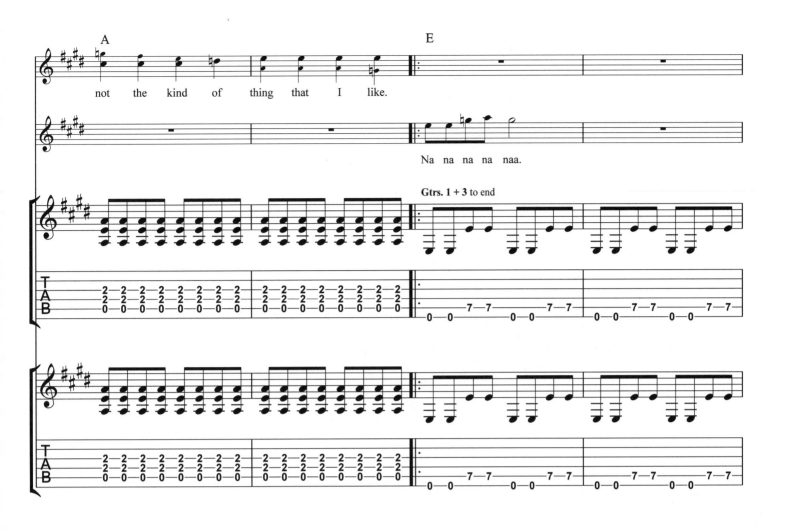

not the kind of thing that I like.

Na na na na naa.

Gtrs. 1 + 3 to end

Na na na na naa.

Oh. ____

You Can Have It All

Words & Music by Nicholas Hodgson, Richard Wilson,
Andrew White, James Rix & Nicholas Baines

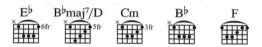

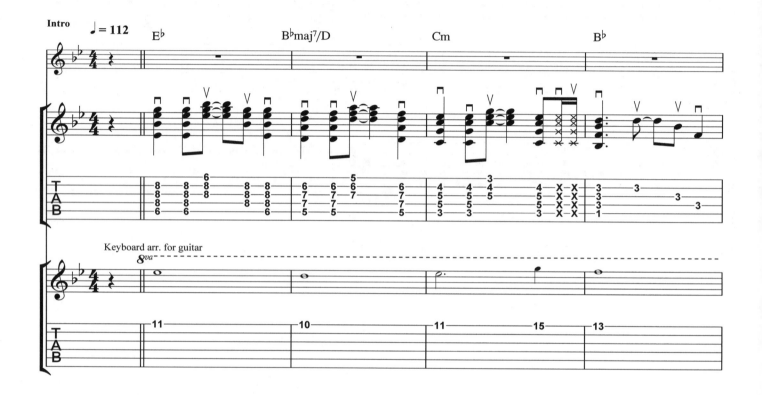

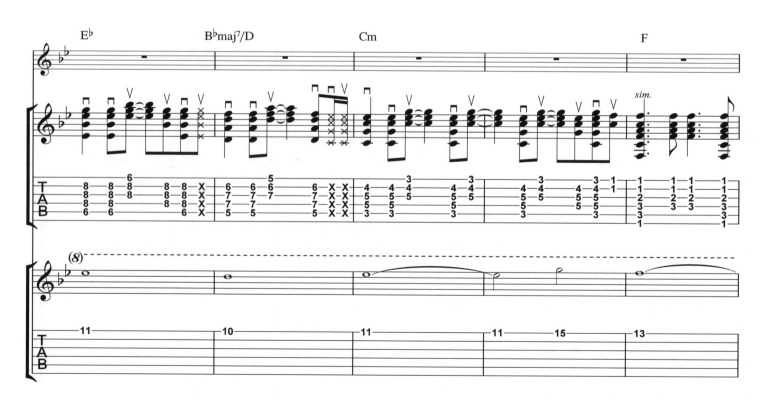

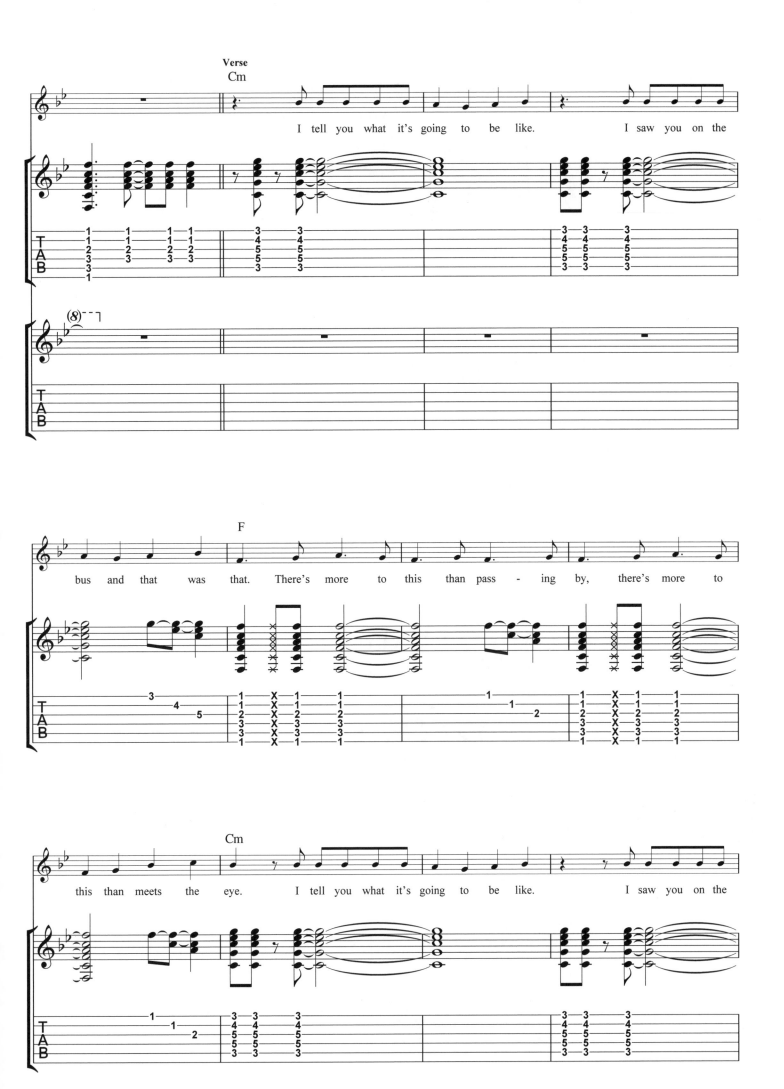

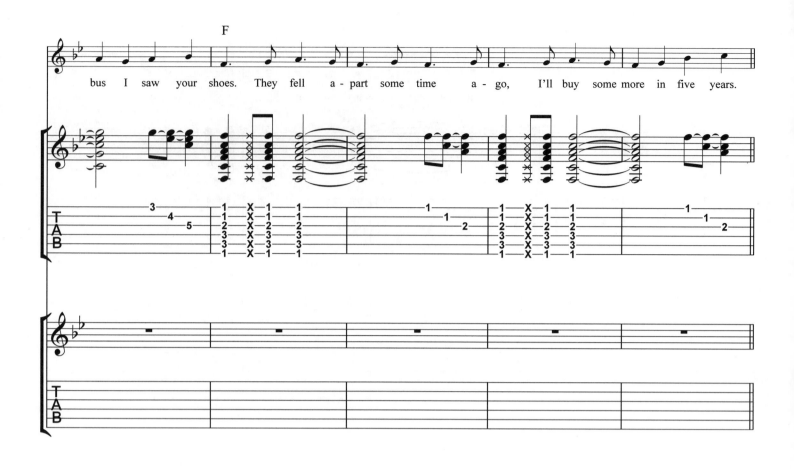

bus I saw your shoes. They fell a - part some time a - go, I'll buy some more in five years.

Bridge

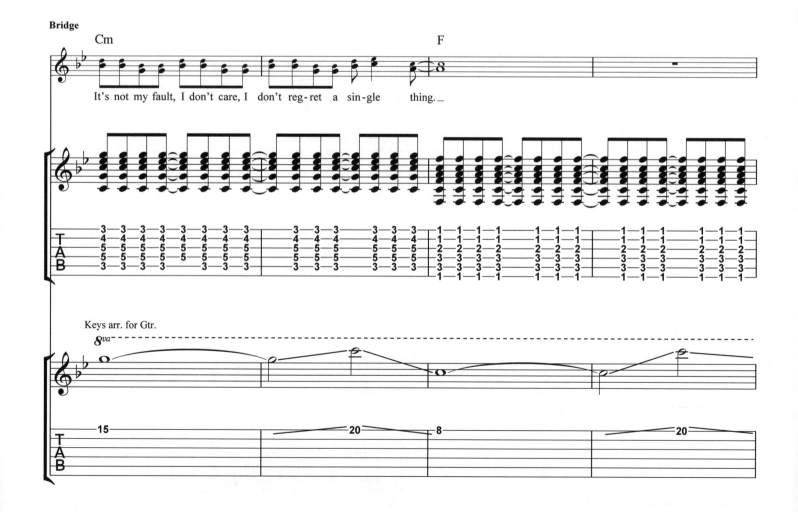

It's not my fault, I don't care, I don't reg-ret a sin-gle thing.

Keys arr. for Gtr.

44

late at night, not by my side 'cos I'm not there to hold you too tight -

- ly. I tell you what it's going to be like, though you can ne-ver hold my hand in pub-lic.

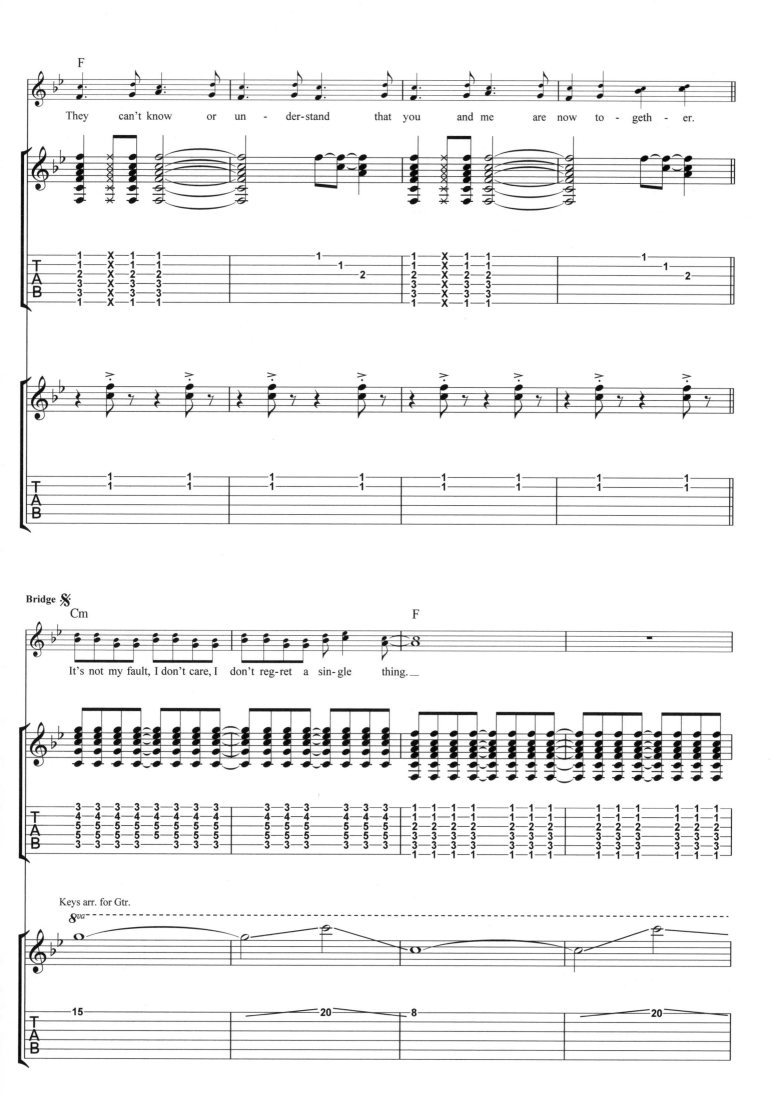

47

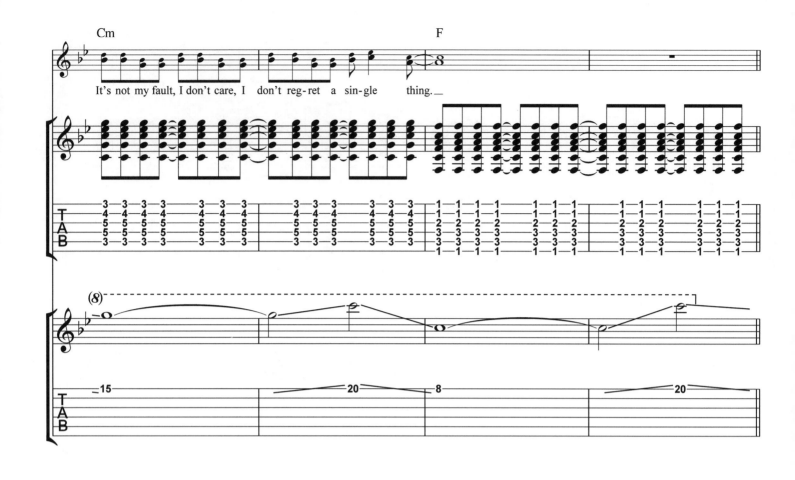

Chorus

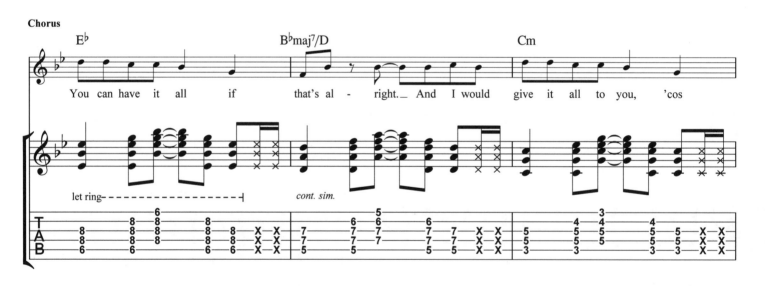

You can have it all if that's al - right._ And I would give it all to you, 'cos

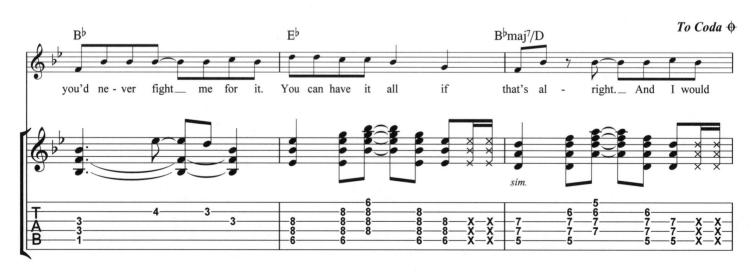

you'd ne - ver fight_ me for it. You can have it all if that's al - right._ And I would

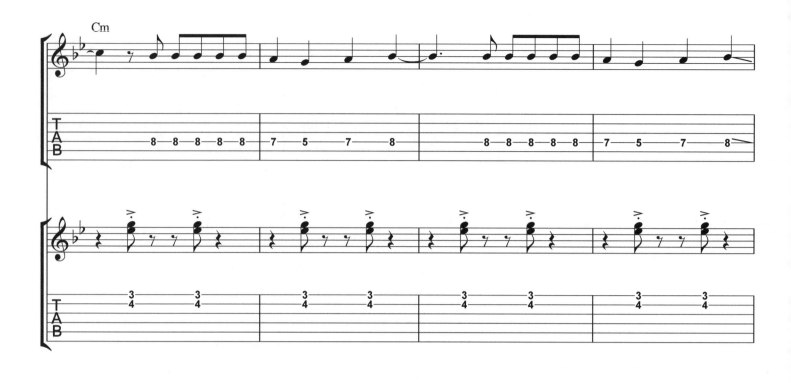

D.S. al Coda

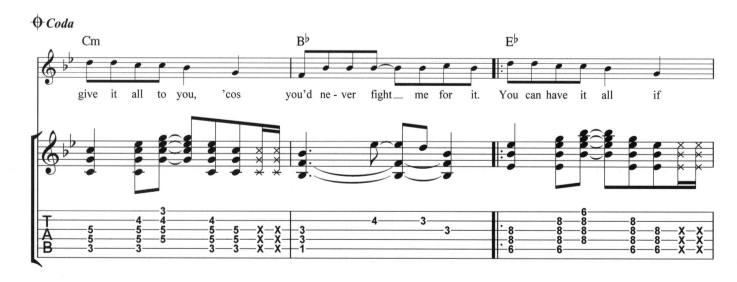

give it all to you, 'cos   you'd ne - ver fight__ me for it.   You can have it all   if

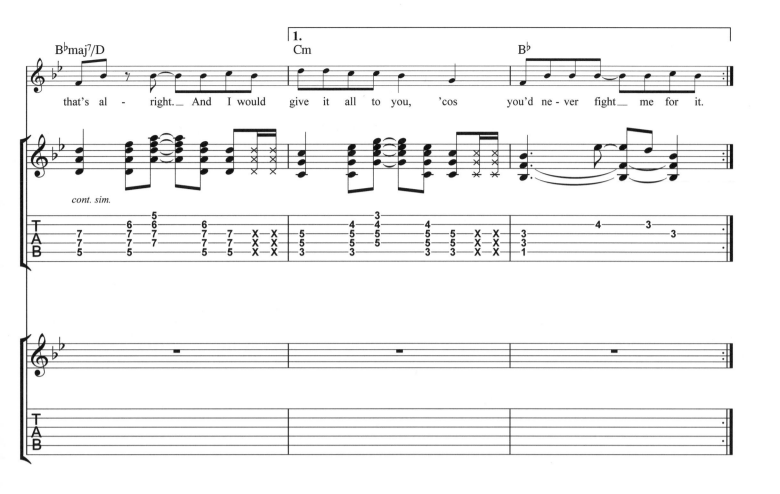

that's al - right.__ And I would give it all to you, 'cos you'd ne - ver fight__ me for it.

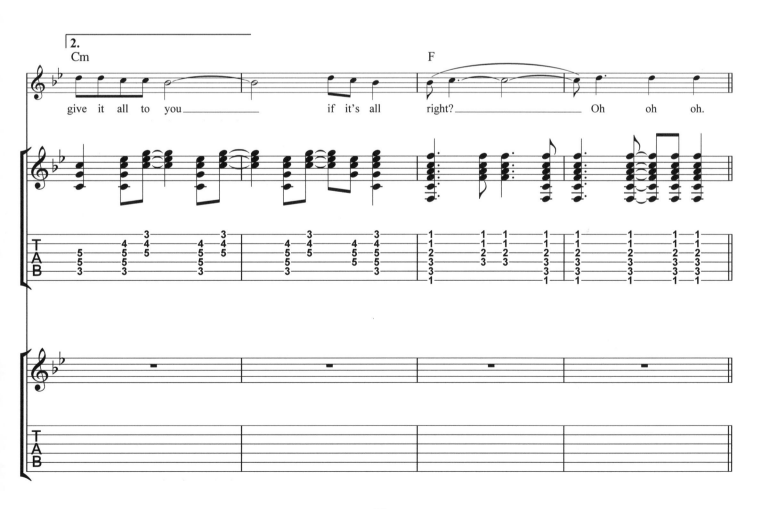

give it all to you_____ if it's all right?_____ Oh oh oh.

Outro

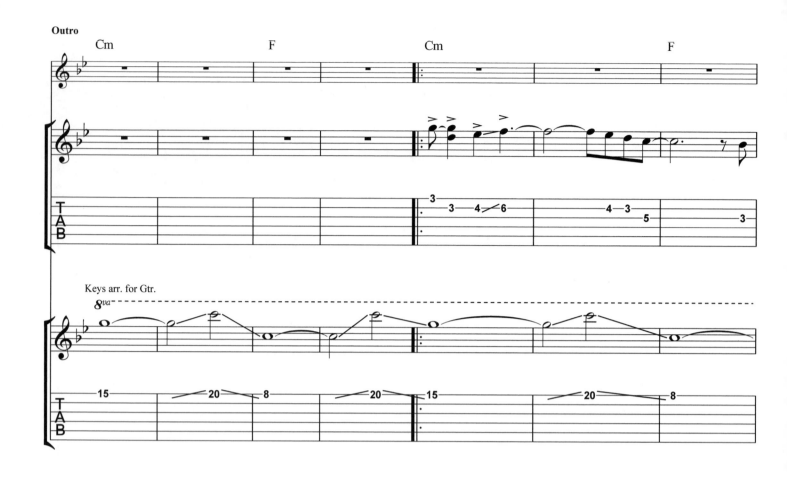

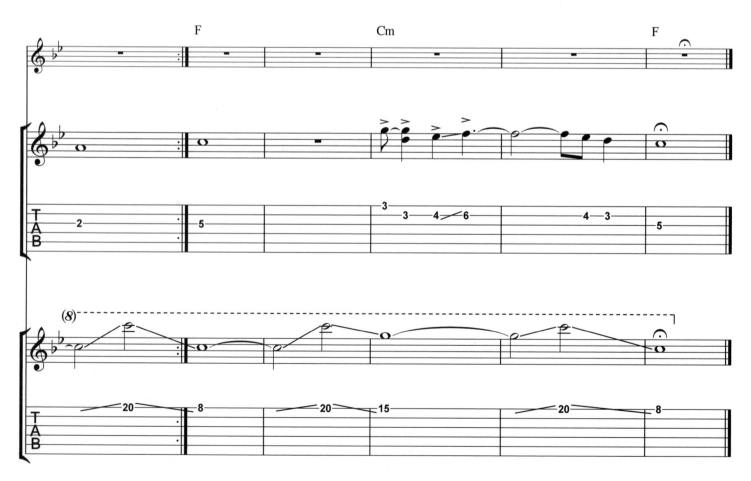

Oh My God

Words & Music by Nicholas Hodgson, Richard Wilson, Andrew White, James Rix & Nicholas Baines

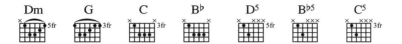

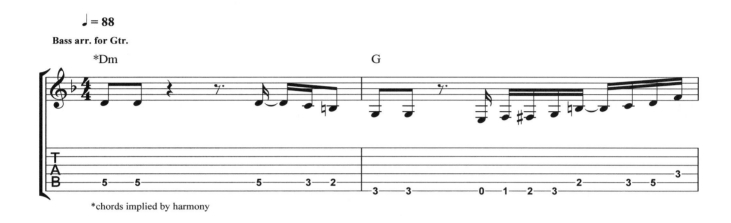

*chords implied by harmony

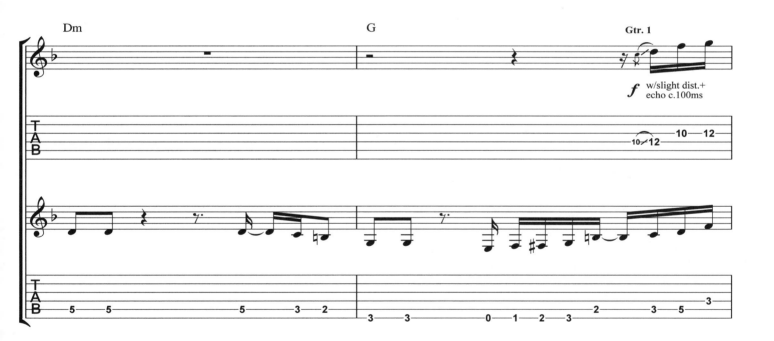

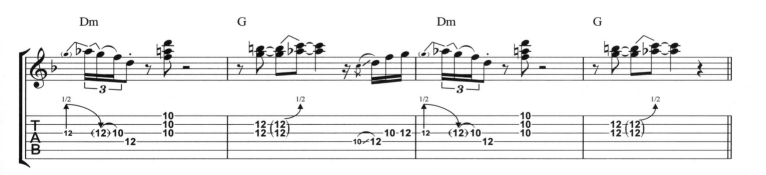

55

Born To Be A Dancer

Words & Music by Nicholas Hodgson, Richard Wilson,
Andrew White, James Rix & Nicholas Baines

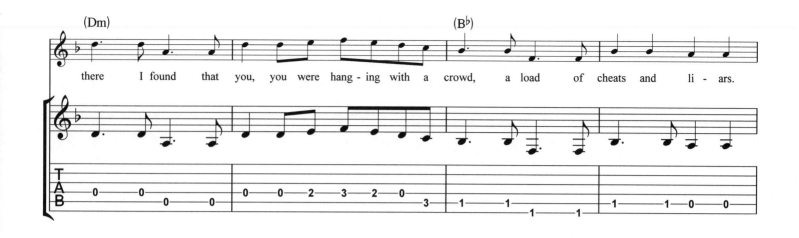

there I found that you, you were hang-ing with a crowd, a load of cheats and li - ars.

Chorus

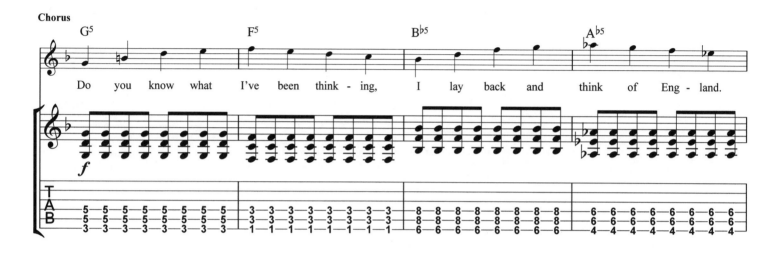

Do you know what I've been think - ing, I lay back and think of Eng - land.

Do you know my re - al ans - wer, I was born to be a dan - cer.

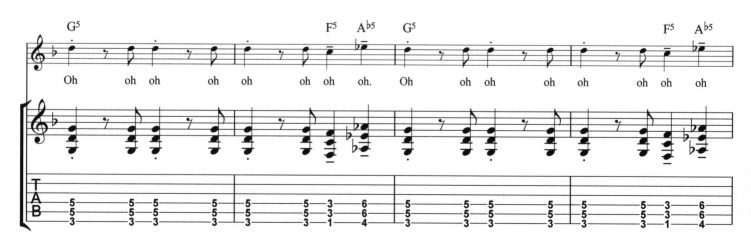

Oh oh oh oh oh oh oh oh. Oh oh oh oh oh oh oh oh

*Chords implied by harmony

Once you asked me what I'm think - ing,

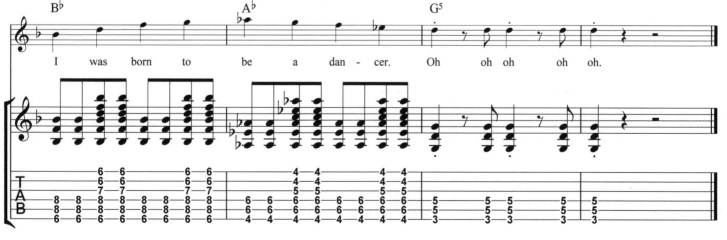

Saturday Night

Words & Music by Nicholas Hodgson, Richard Wilson,
Andrew White, James Rix & Nicholas Baines

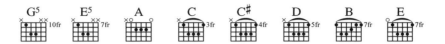

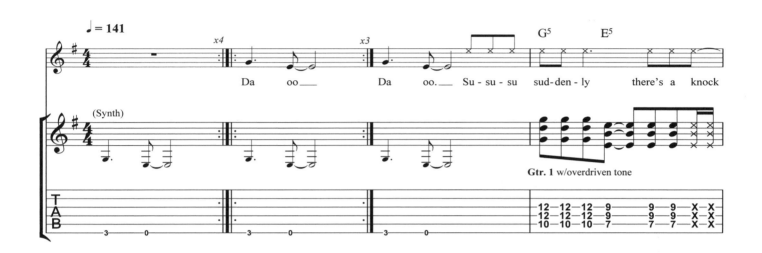

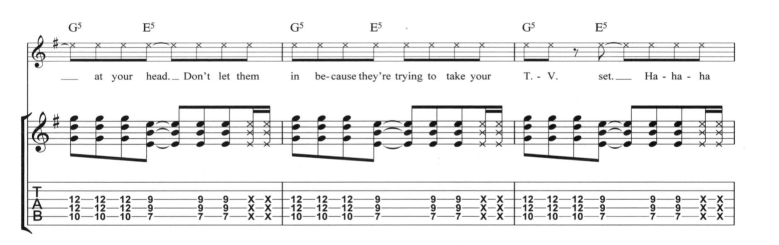

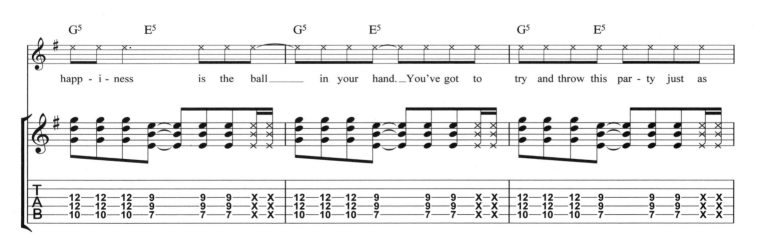

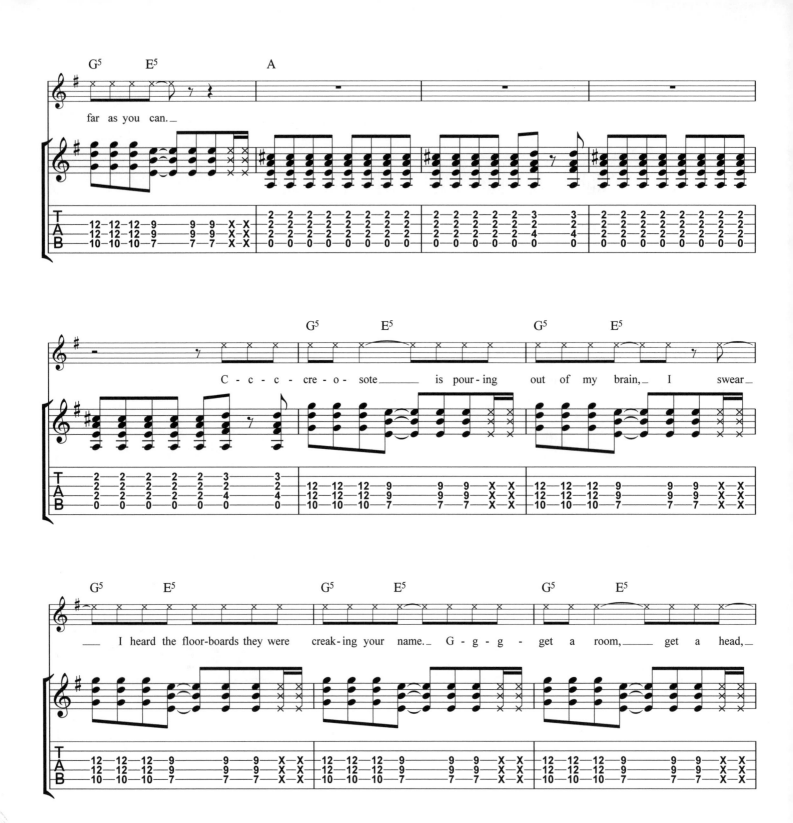

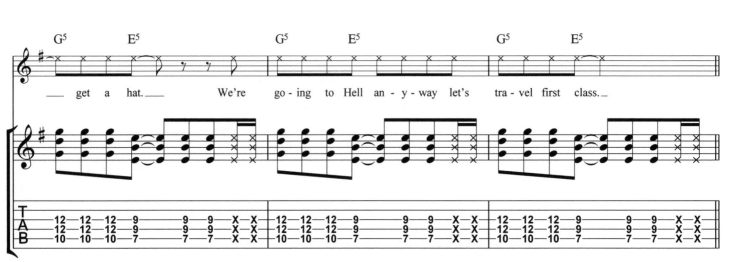

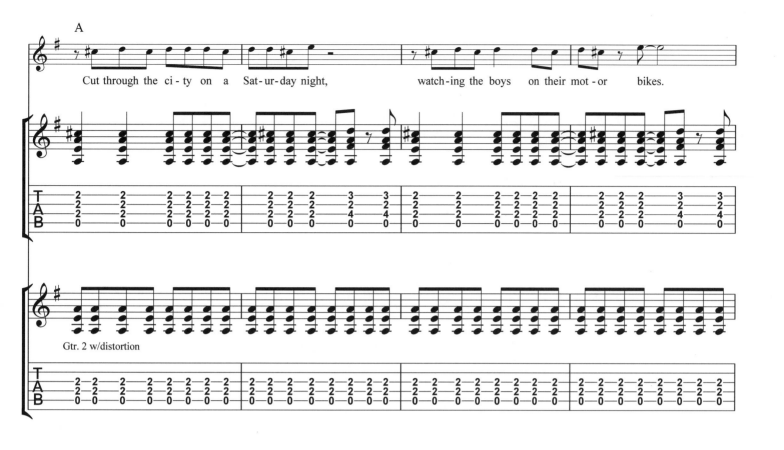

Cut through the ci - ty on a Sat - ur - day night, watch - ing the boys on their mot - or bikes.

Gtr. 2 w/distortion

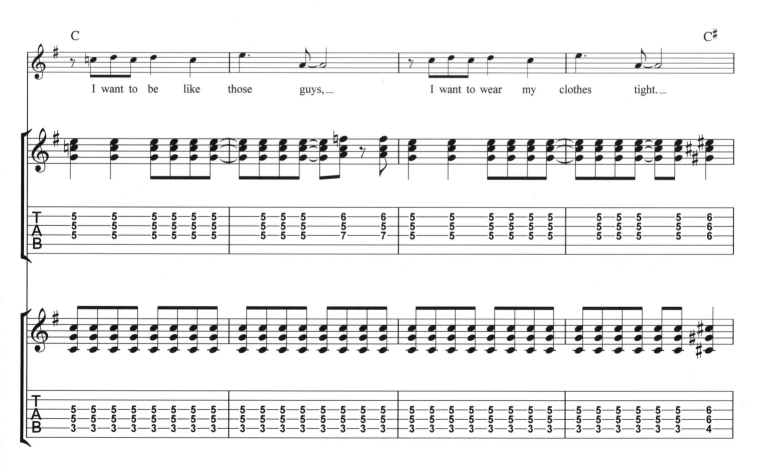

I want to be like those guys, __ I want to wear my clothes tight. __

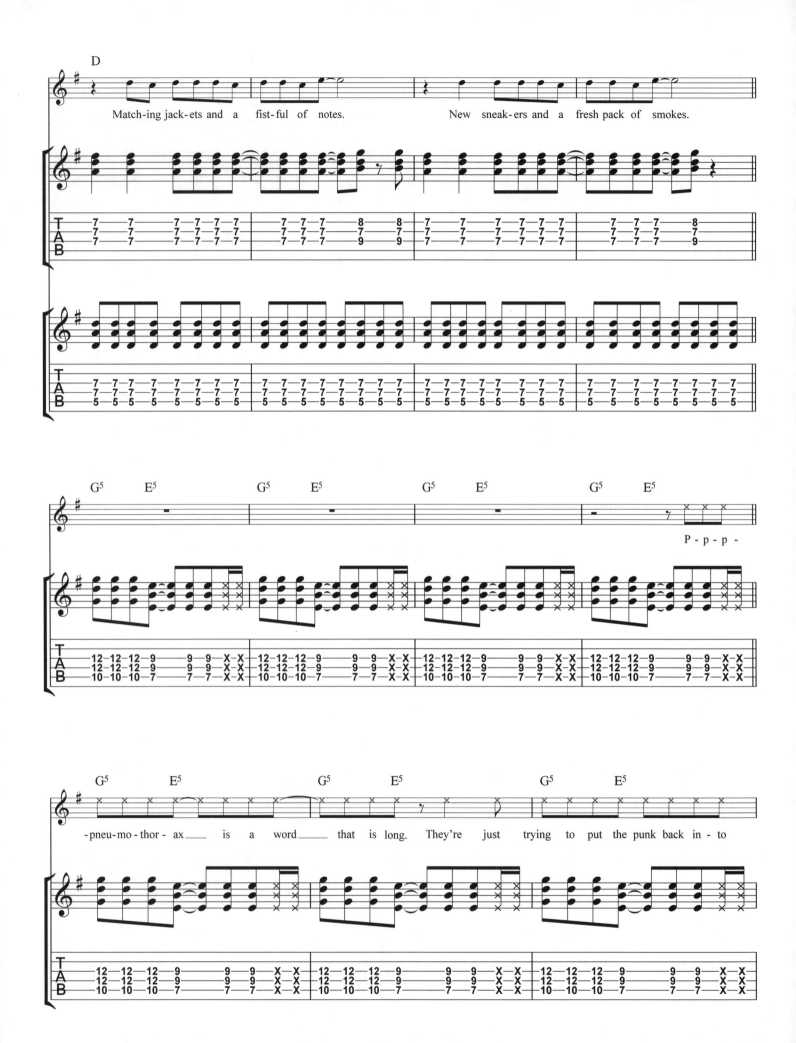

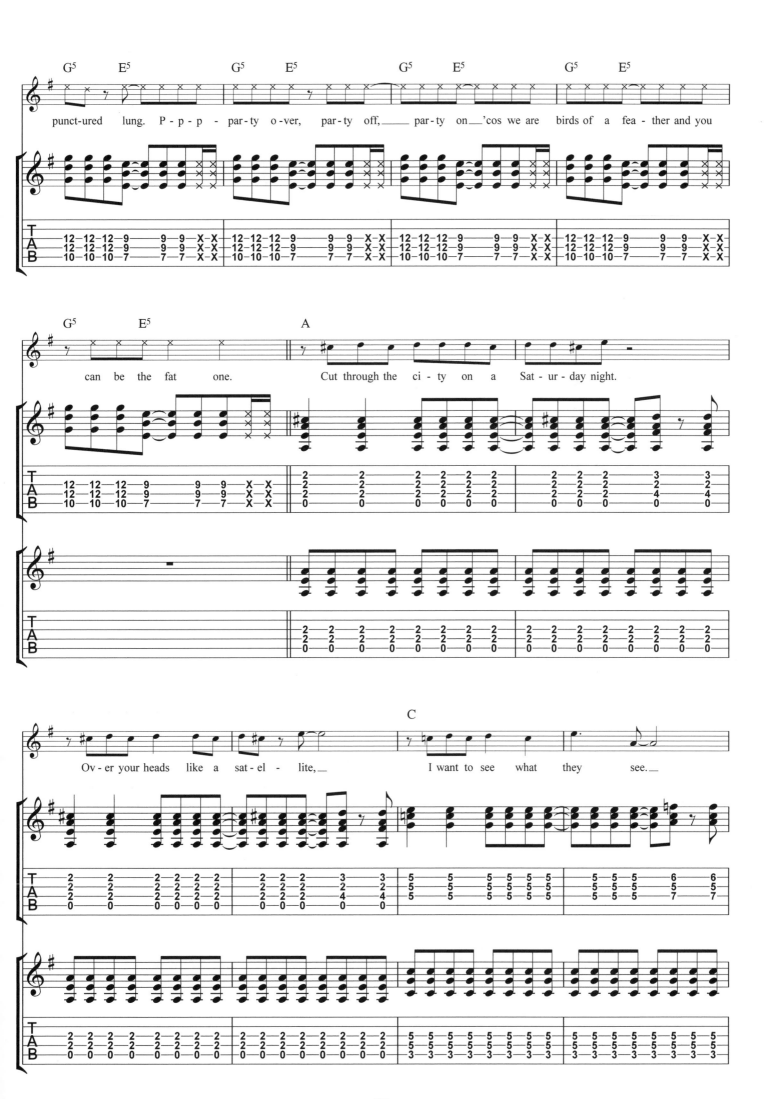

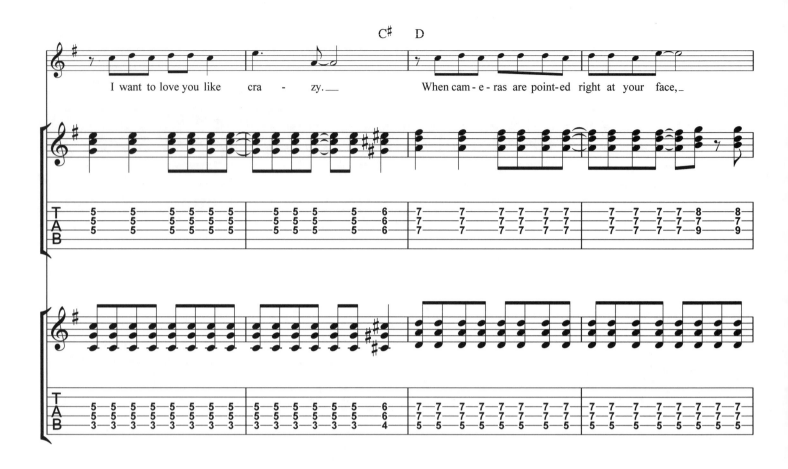

I want to love you like cra - zy.___ When cam - e - ras are point-ed right at your face,___

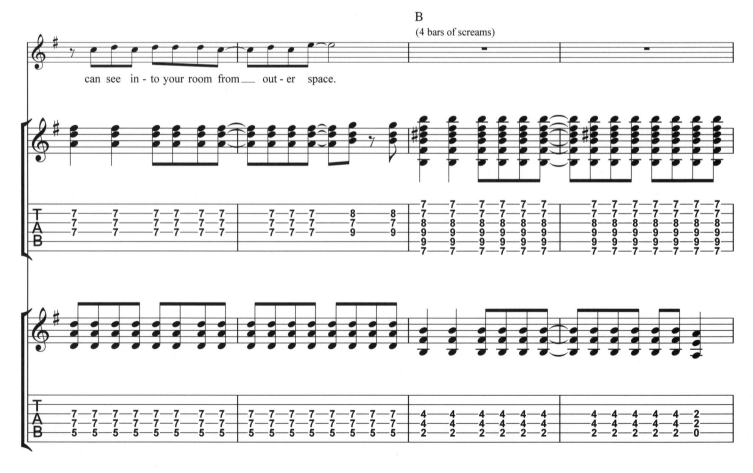

can see in - to your room from ___ out - er space.

(4 bars of screams)

68

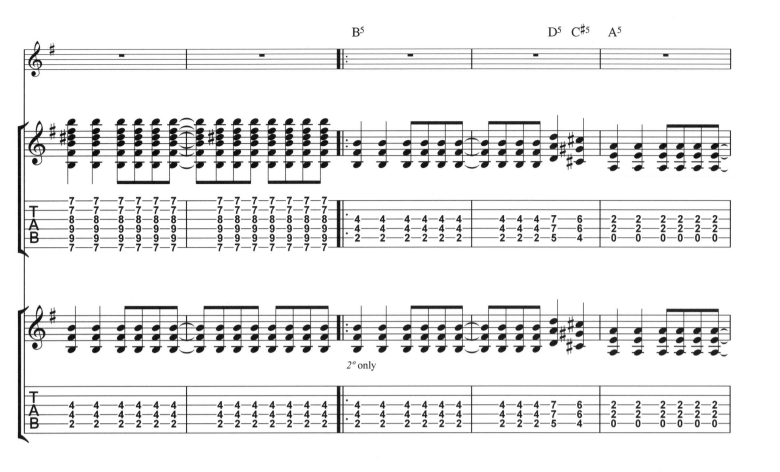

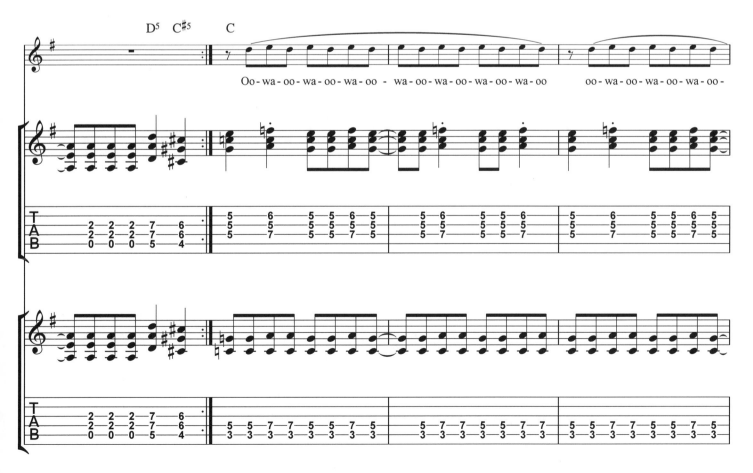

-wa-oo-wa-oo-wa-oo - wa-oo   oo-wa-oo-wa-oo-wa-oo - wa-oo-wa-oo-wa-oo-wa-oo   oo-wa-oo-wa-oo-wa-oo-

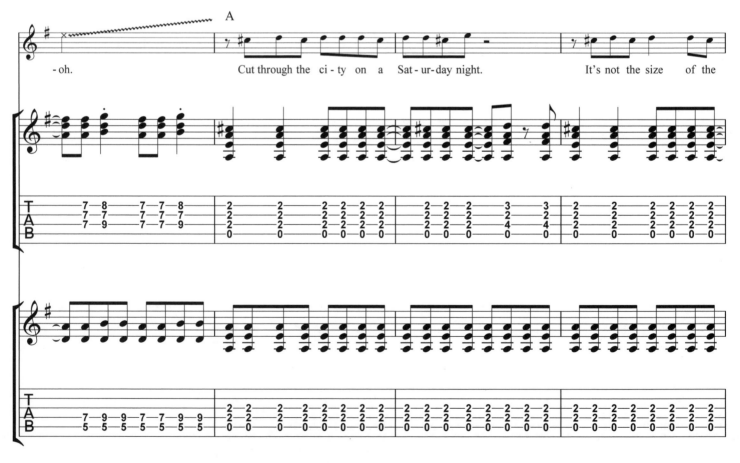

-oh.   Cut through the ci-ty on a Sat-ur-day night.   It's not the size of the

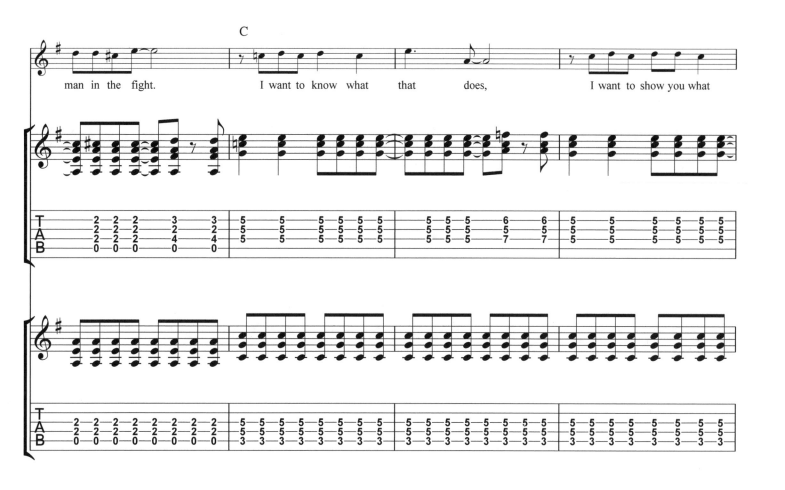

man in the fight.   I want to know what that   does,   I want to show you what

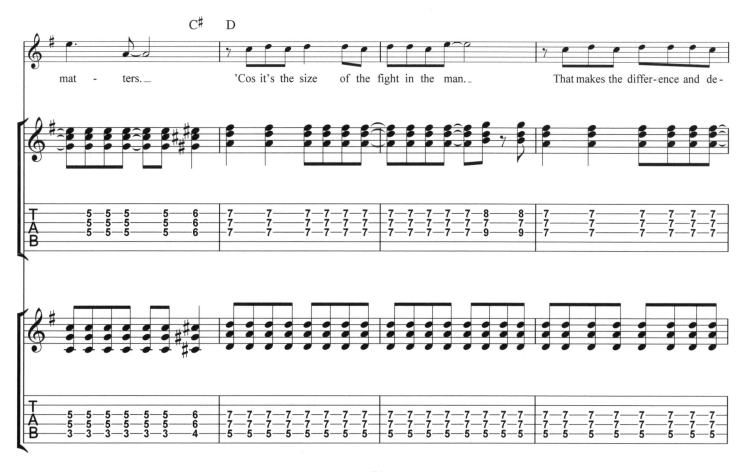

mat - ters.＿   'Cos it's the size   of the fight in the man.＿   That makes the differ-ence and de-

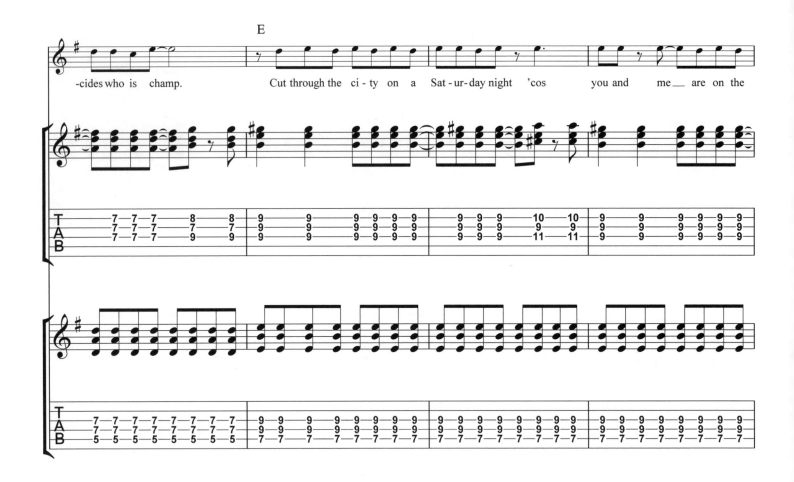

-cides who is champ.   Cut through the ci-ty on a Sat-ur-day night 'cos   you and   me   are on the

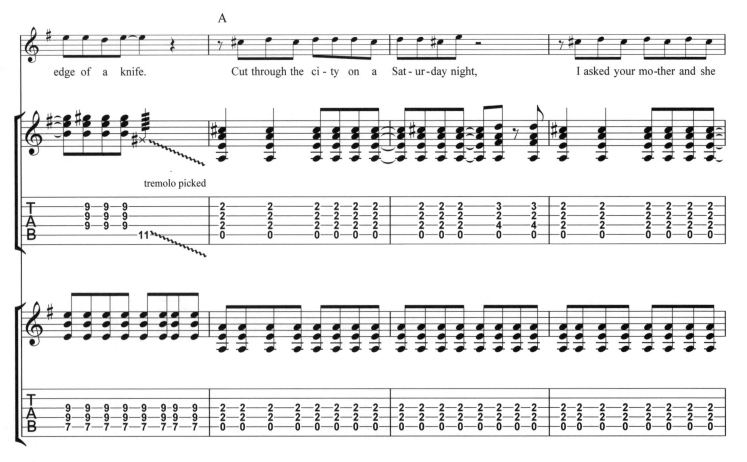

edge of a knife.   Cut through the ci-ty on a Sat-ur-day night,   I asked your mo-ther and she

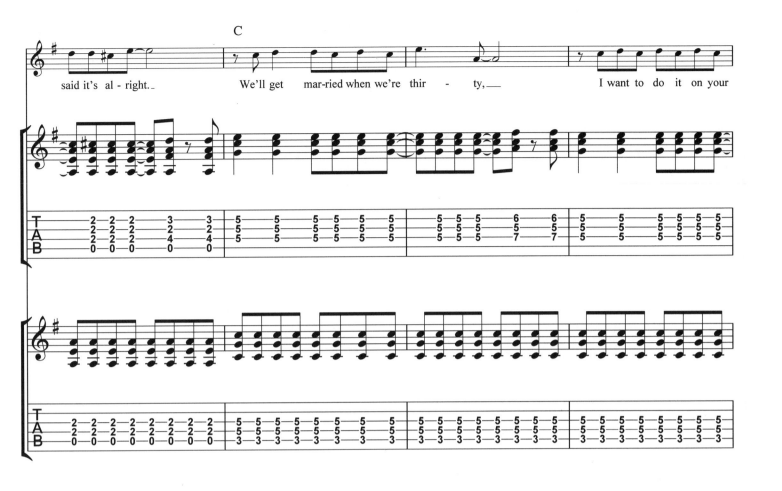

said it's al - right.___ We'll get mar-ried when we're thir - ty,___ I want to do it on your

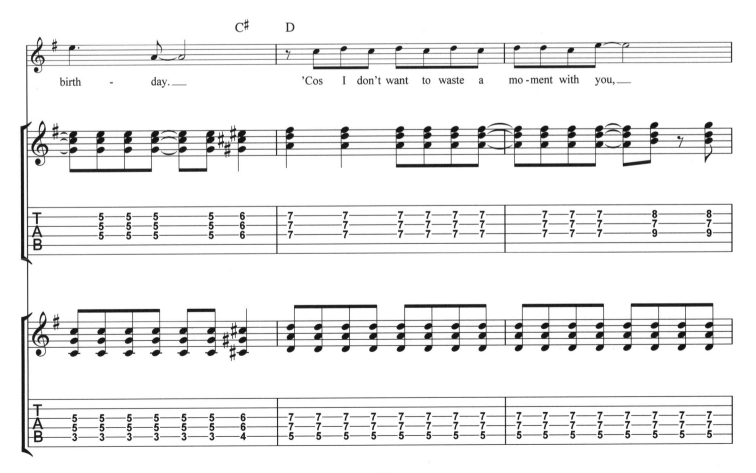

birth - day.___ 'Cos I don't want to waste a mo -ment with you,___

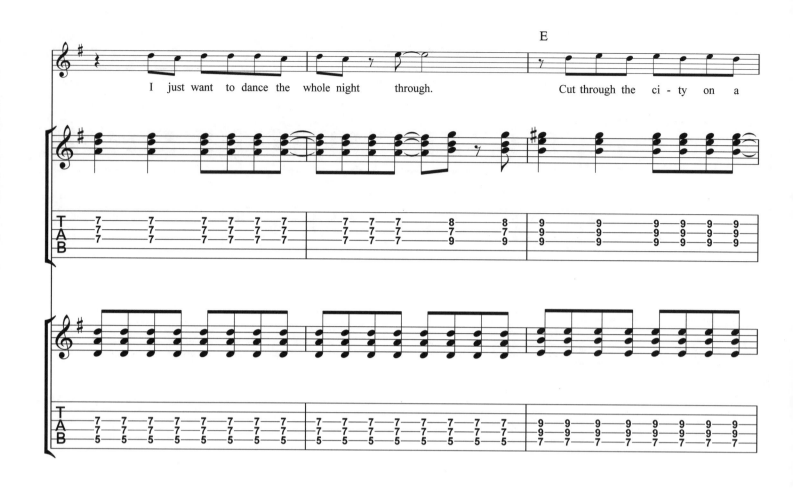

I just want to dance the whole night through. Cut through the ci - ty on a

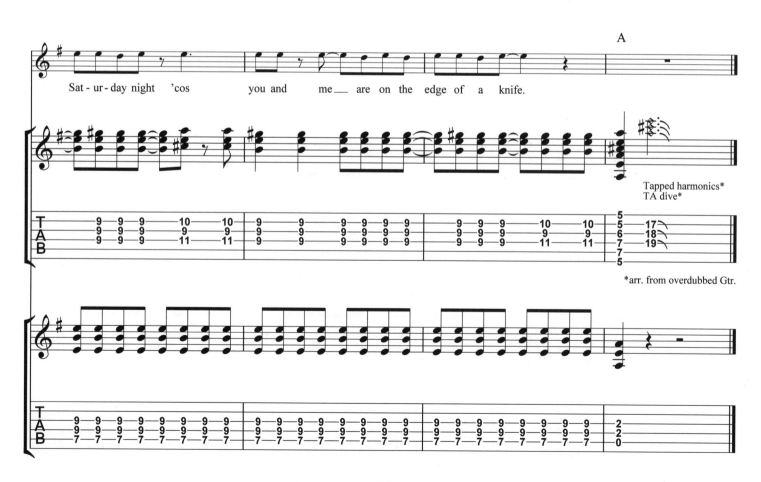

Sat - ur - day night 'cos you and me are on the edge of a knife.

Tapped harmonics*
TA dive*

*arr. from overdubbed Gtr.

What Did I Ever Give You?

Words & Music by Nicholas Hodgson, Richard Wilson,
Andrew White, James Rix & Nicholas Baines

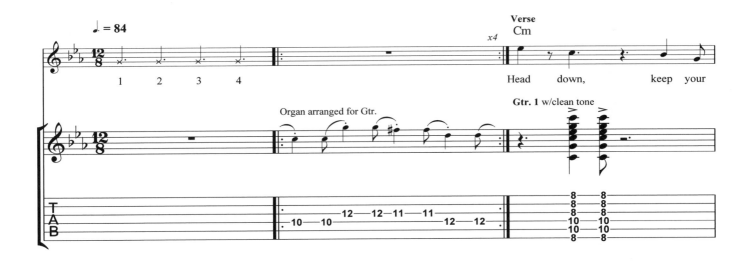

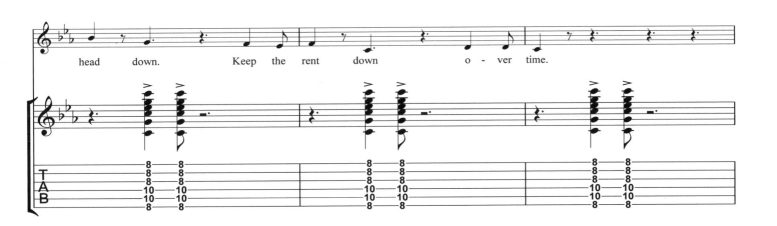

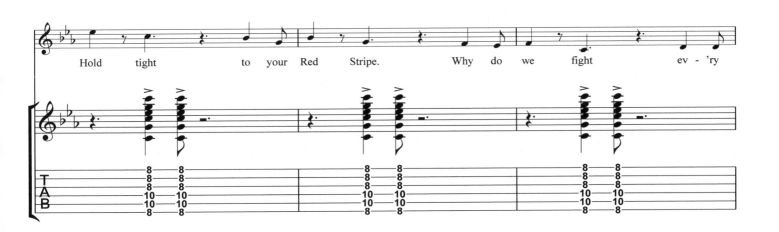

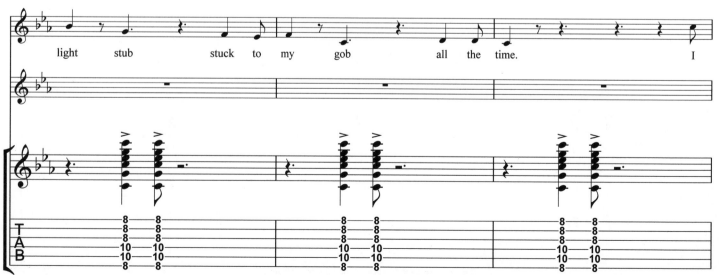

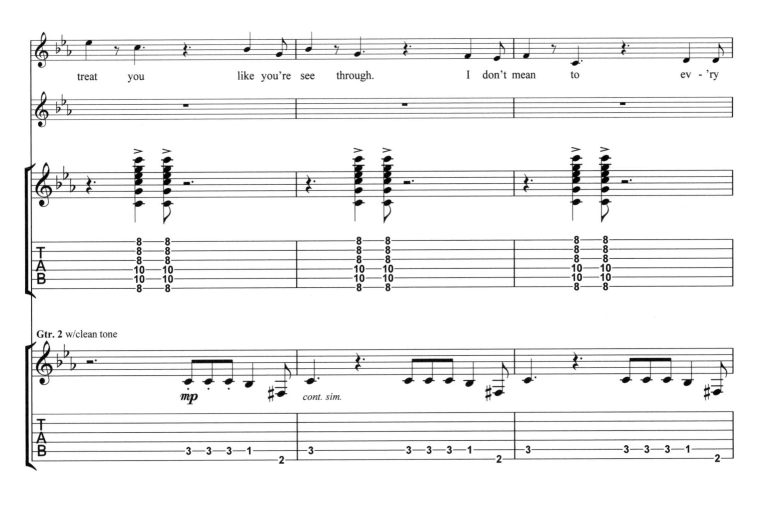

treat you like you're see through. I don't mean to ev - 'ry

Gtr. 2 w/clean tone

mp *cont. sim.*

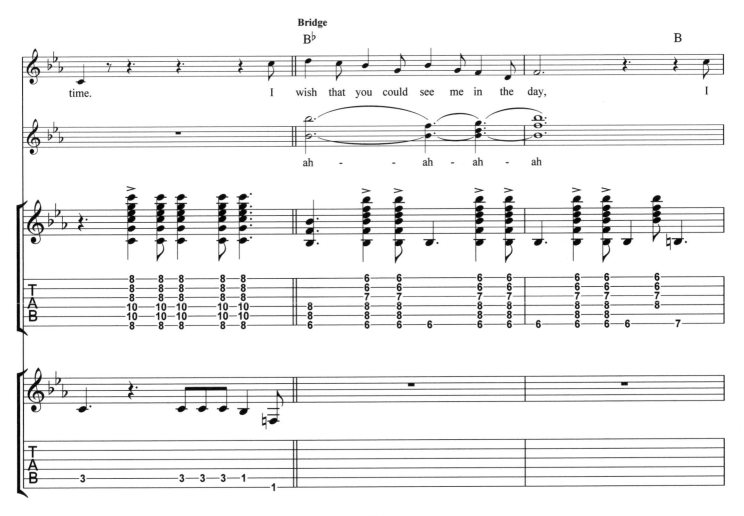

time.

Bridge

B♭

I wish that you could see me in the day, I

ah - ah - ah - ah

B

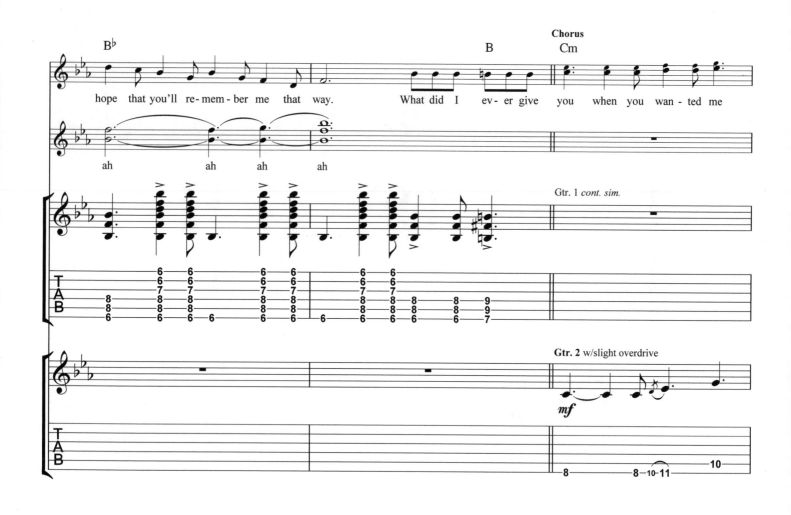

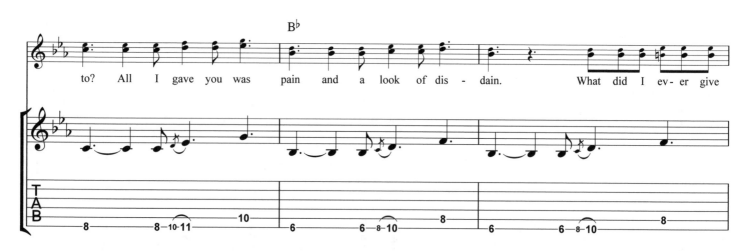

80

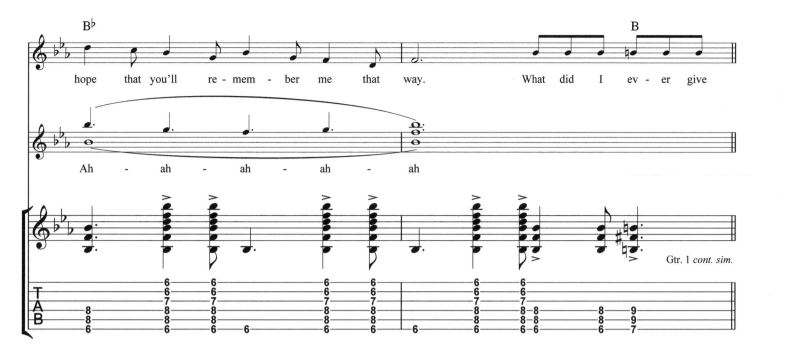

Chorus

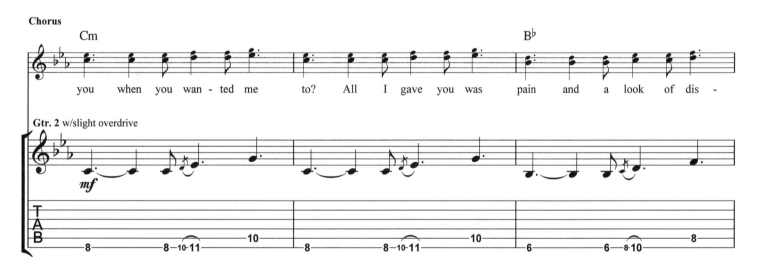

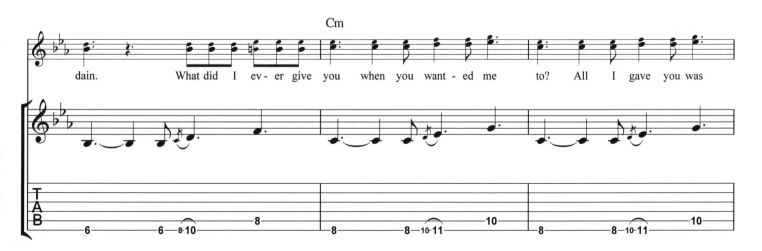

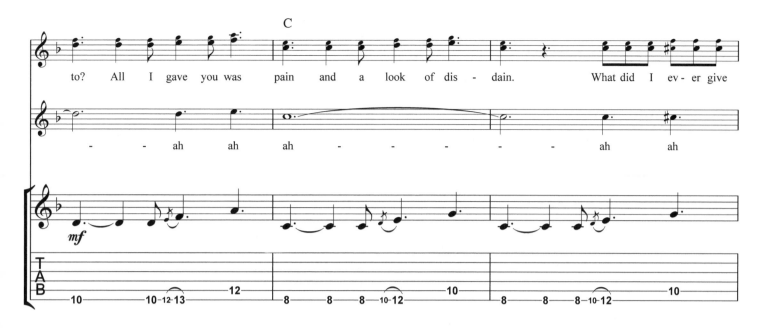

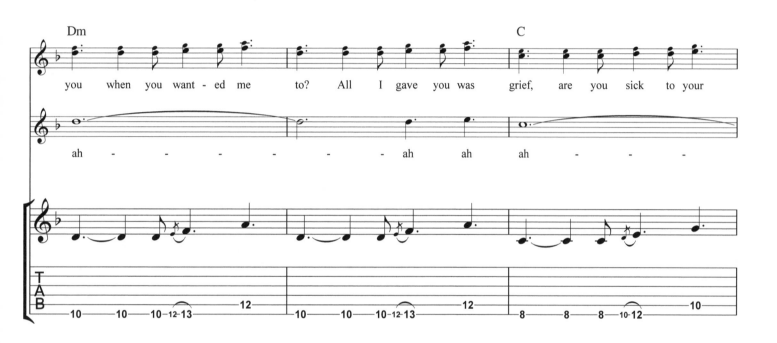

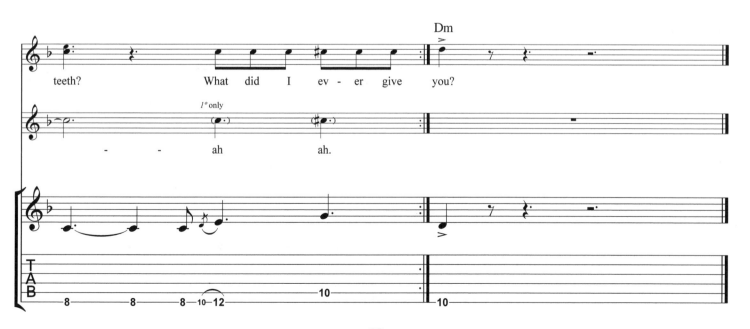

Time Honoured Tradition

Words & Music by Nicholas Hodgson, Richard Wilson,
Andrew White, James Rix & Nicholas Baines

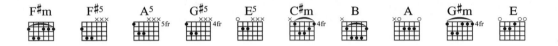

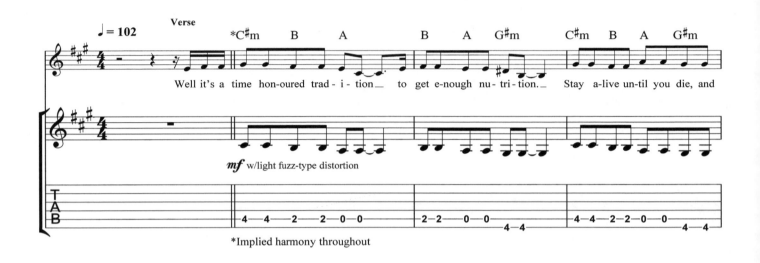

*Implied harmony throughout

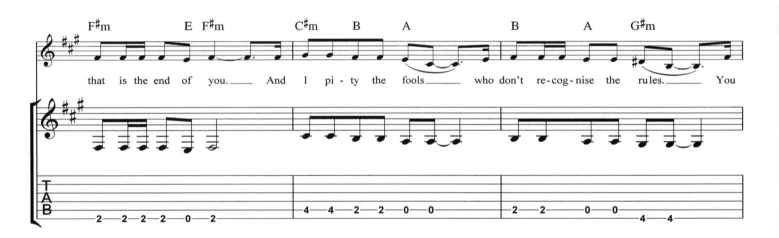

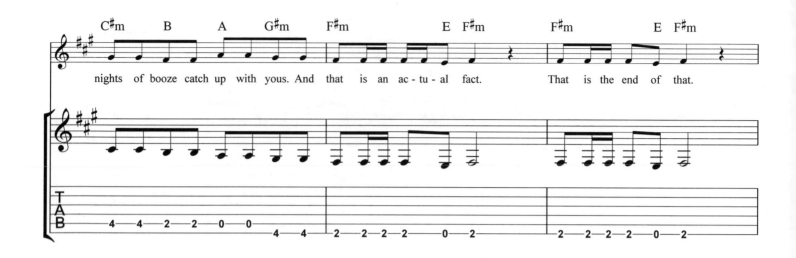

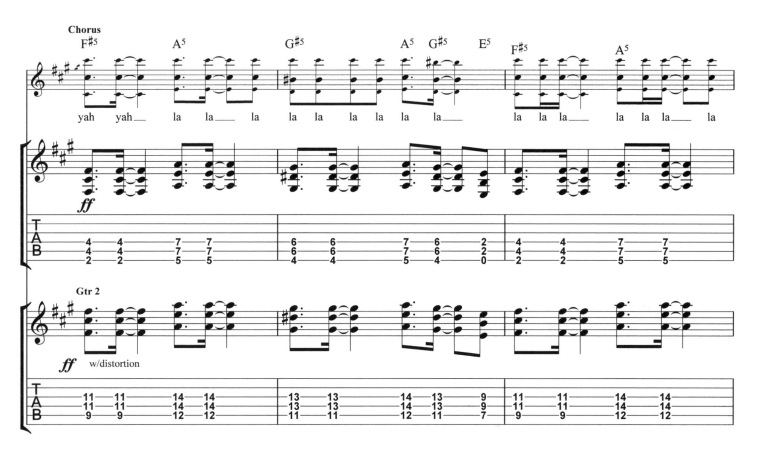

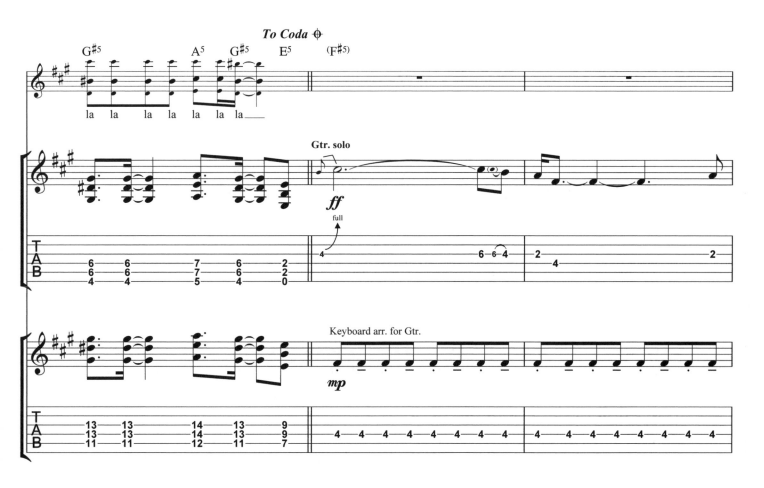

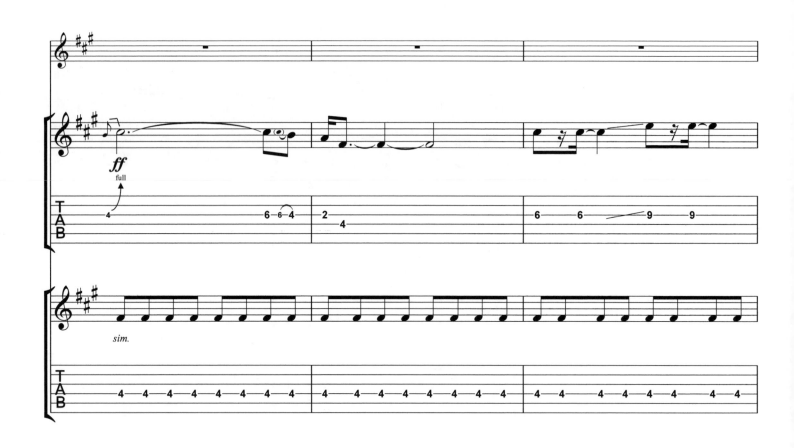

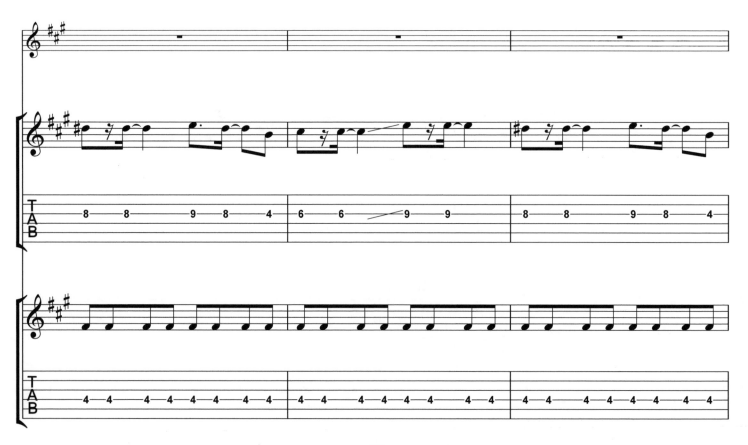

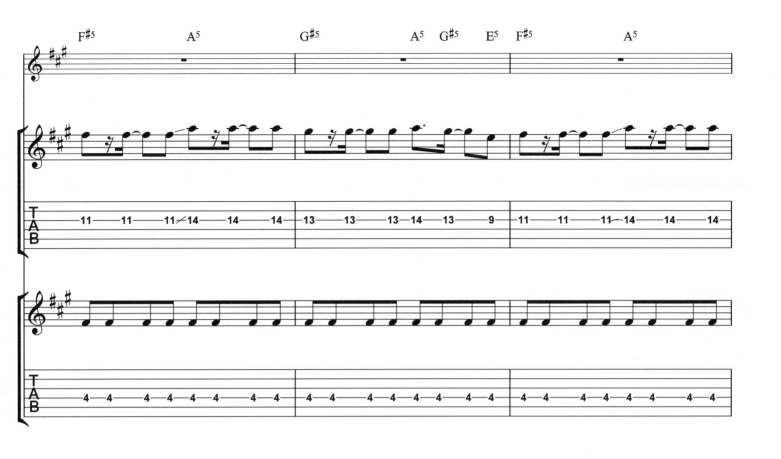

Interlude

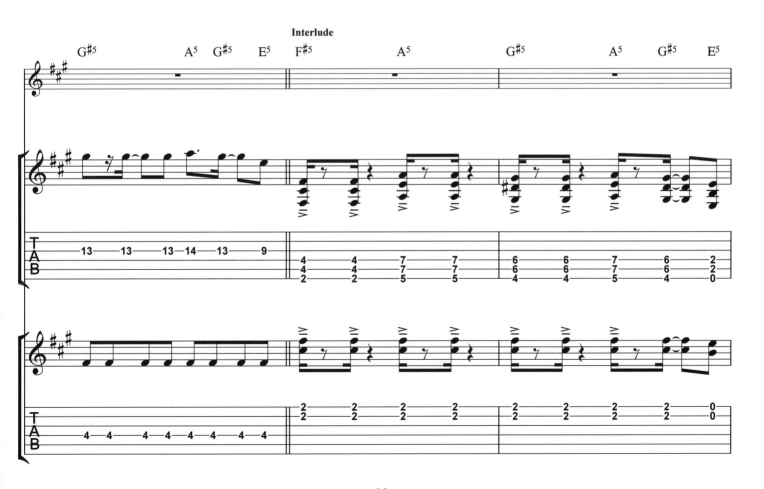

89

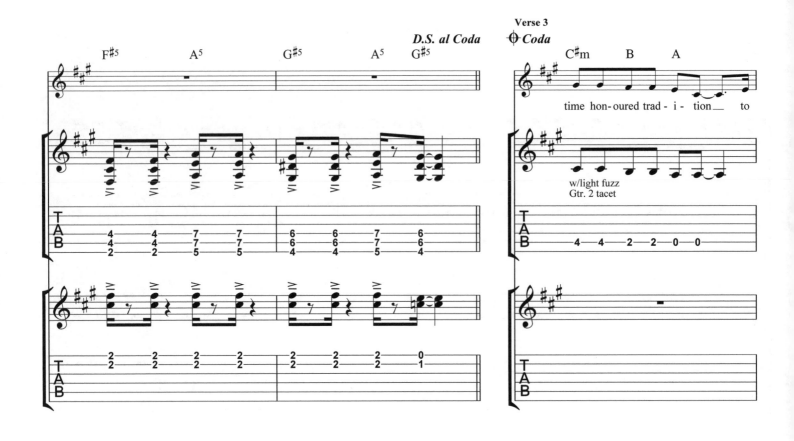

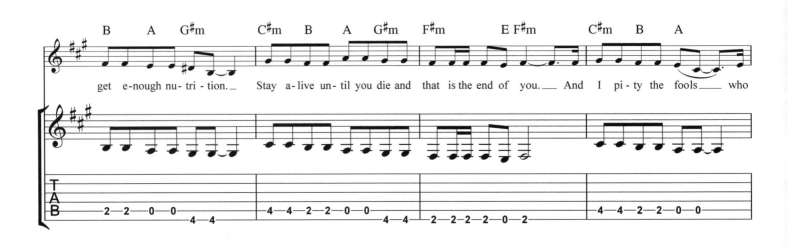

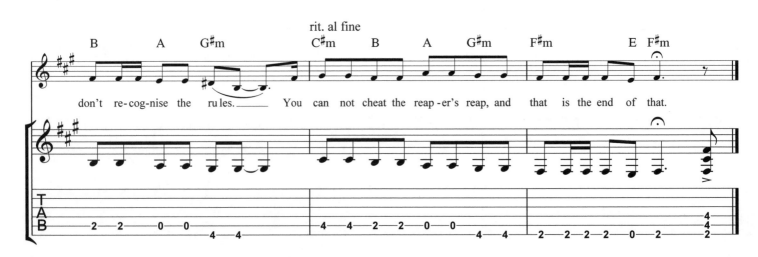

Caroline, Yes

Words & Music by Nicholas Hodgson, Richard Wilson,
Andrew White, James Rix & Nicholas Baines

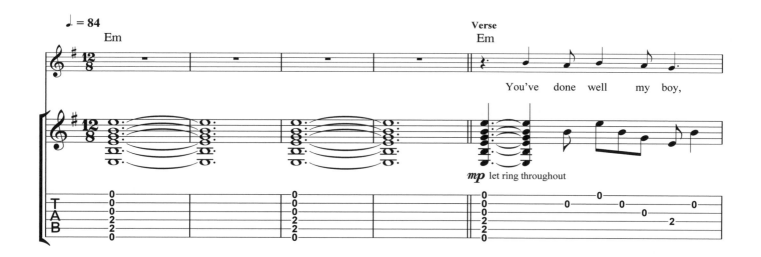

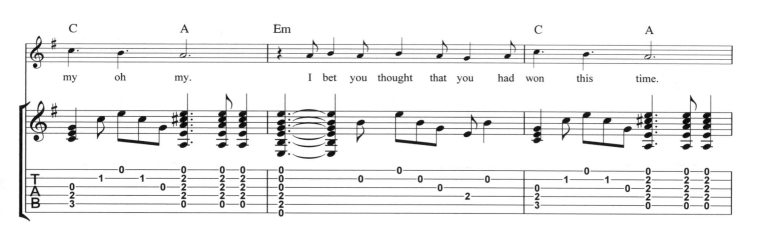

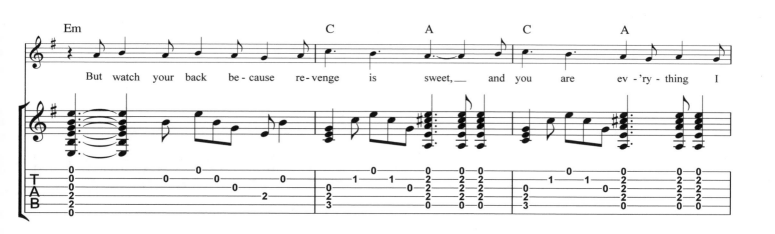

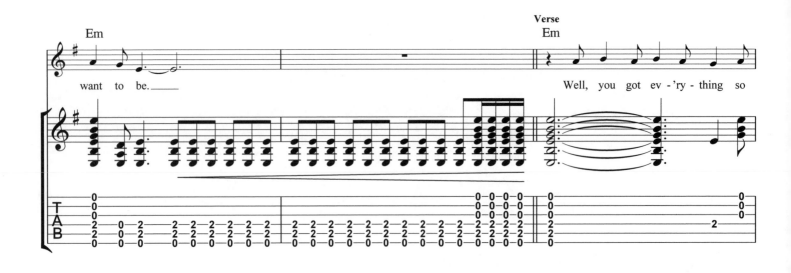

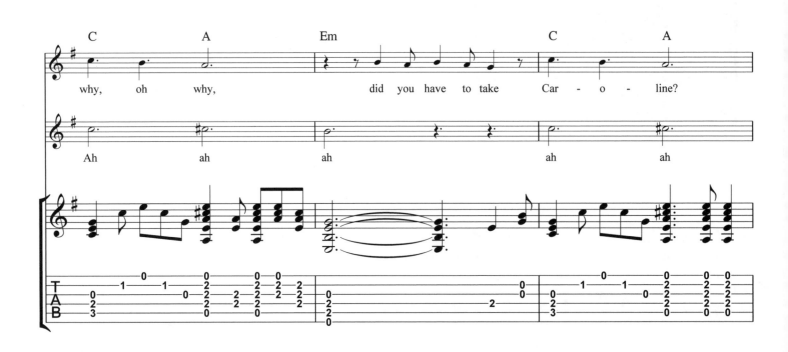

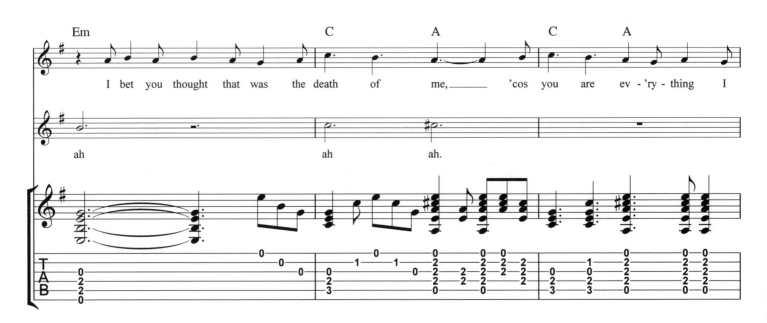

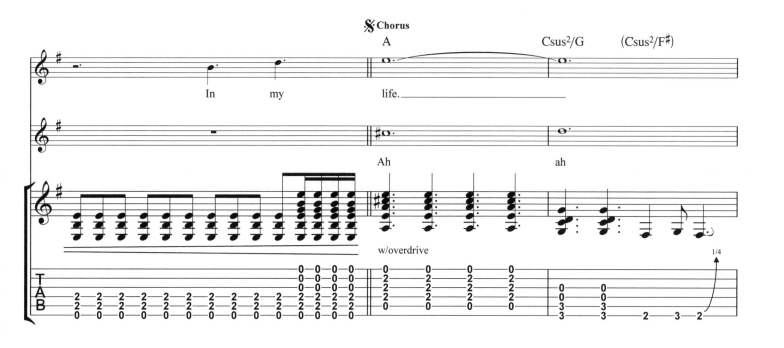

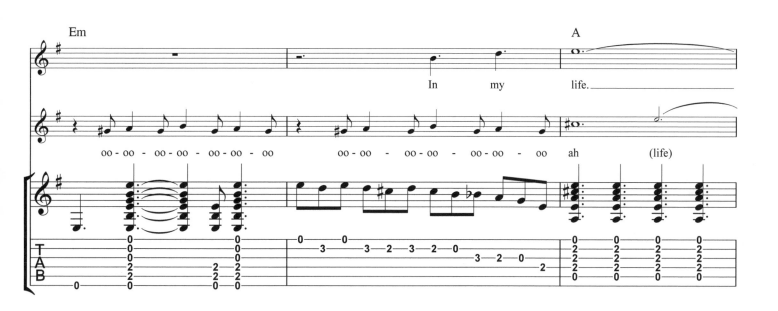

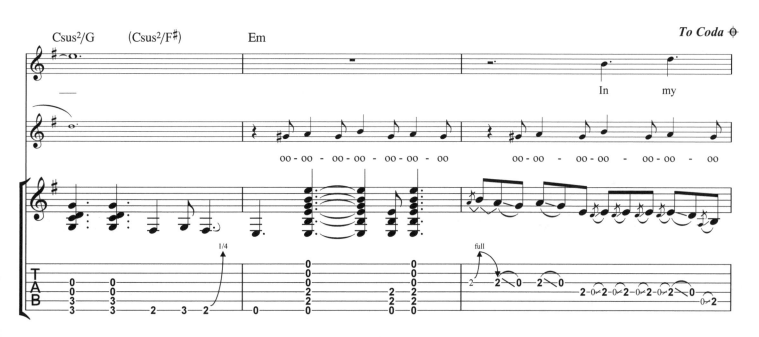

97

Team Mate

Words & Music by Nicholas Hodgson, Richard Wilson,
Andrew White, James Rix & Nicholas Baines

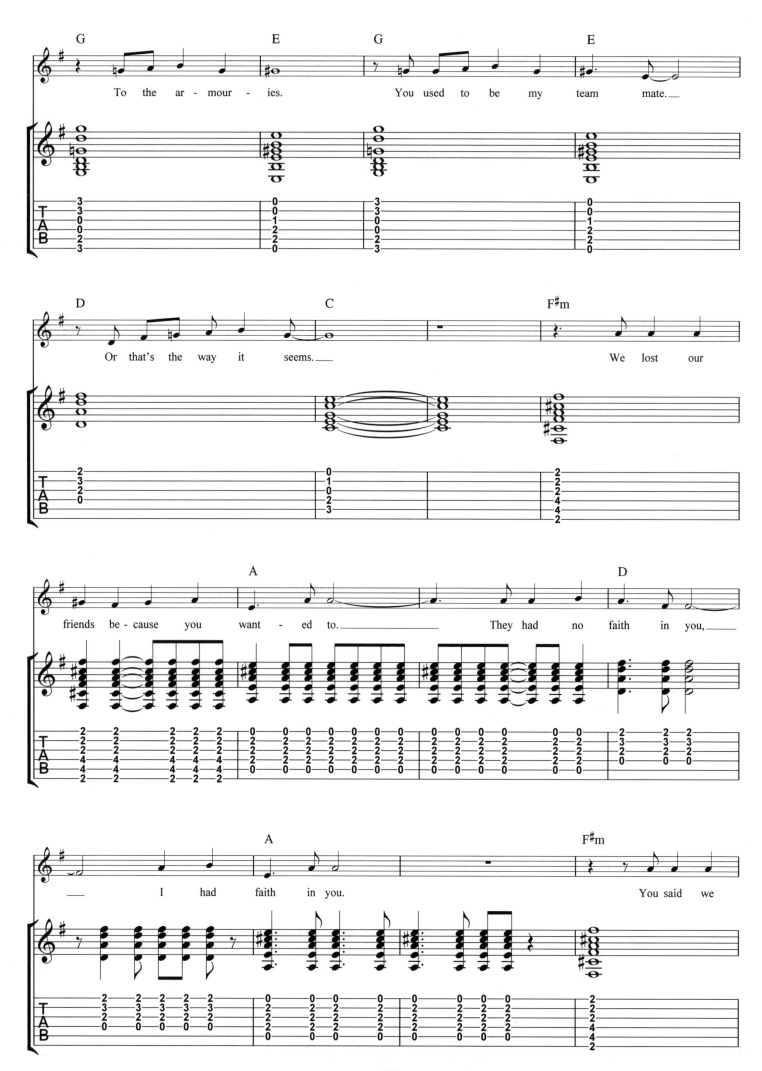

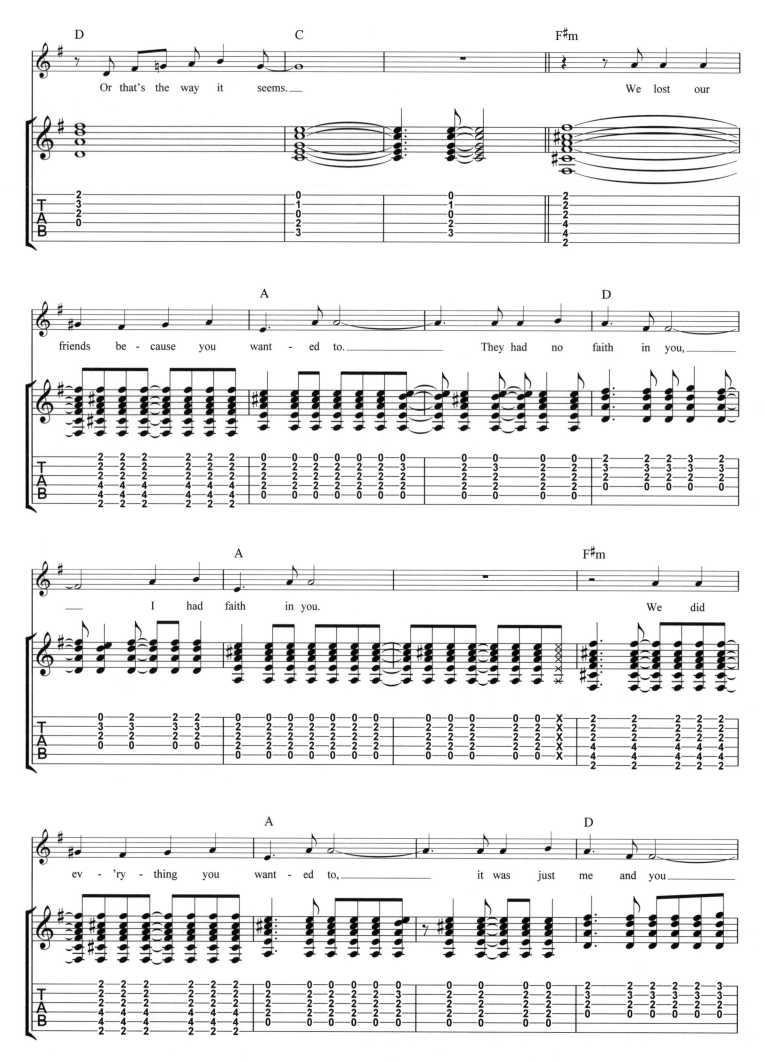

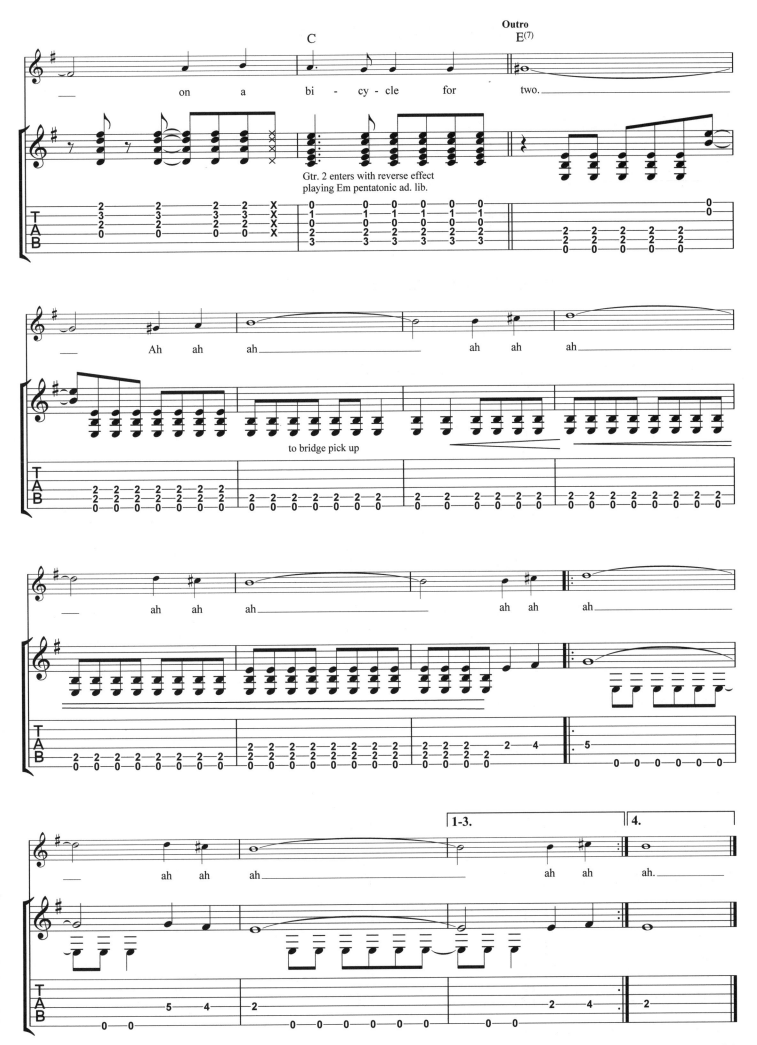

3 4 5 6 7 8 9
1/06(57409)

Guitar Tabalature Explained

Guitar music can be notated in three different ways: on a musical stave, in tablature, and in rhythm slashes

RHYTHM SLASHES are written above the stave. Strum chords in the rhythm indicated. Round noteheads indicate single notes.

THE MUSICAL STAVE shows pitches and rhythms and is divided by lines into bars. Pitches are named after the first seven letters of the alphabet.

TABLATURE graphically represents the guitar fingerboard. Each horizontal line represents a string, and each number represents a fret.

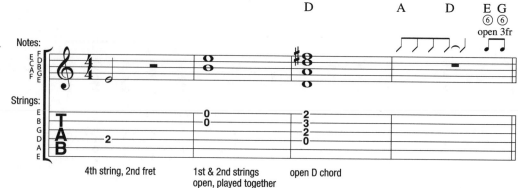

4th string, 2nd fret

1st & 2nd strings open, played together

open D chord

Definitions For Special Guitar Notation

SEMI-TONE BEND: Strike the note and bend up a semi-tone (1/2 step).

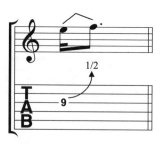

WHOLE-TONE BEND: Strike the note and bend up a whole-tone (whole step).

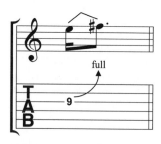

GRACE NOTE BEND: Strike the note and bend as indicated. Play the first note as quickly as possible.

QUARTER-TONE BEND: Strike the note and bend up a 1/4 step.

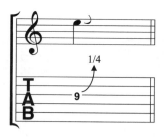

BEND & RELEASE: Strike the note and bend up as indicated, then release back to the original note.

COMPOUND BEND & RELEASE: Strike the note and bend up and down in the rhythm indicated.

PRE-BEND: Bend the note as indicated, then strike it.

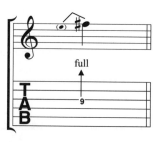

PRE-BEND & RELEASE: Bend the note as indicated. Strike it and release the note back to the original pitch.

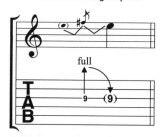

HAMMER-ON: Strike the first note with one finger, then sound the second note (on the same string) with another finger by fretting it without picking.

PULL-OFF: Place both fingers on the notes to be sounded, strike the first note and without picking, pull the finger off to sound the second note.

LEGATO SLIDE (GLISS): Strike the first note and then slide the same fret-hand finger up or down to the second note. The second note is not struck.

MUFFLED STRINGS: A percussive sound is produced by laying the fret hand across the string(s) without depressing, and striking them with the pick hand.

NATURAL HARMONIC: Strike the note while the fret-hand lightly touches the string directly over the fret indicated.

PICK SCRAPE: The edge of the pick is rubbed down (or up) the string, producing a scratchy sound.

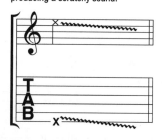

PALM MUTING: The note is partially muted by the pick hand lightly touching the string(s) just before the bridge.

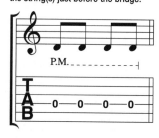

SHIFT SLIDE (GLISS & RESTRIKE): Same as legato slide, except the second note is struck.

NOTE: The speed of any bend is indicated by the music notation and tempo.

104